CW00674829

Corı in Short

A Collection of Cornish Writing

Edited by

Kate Horsley & P. T. McAllister

First published 2024
Inkfish Press
www.inkfishmag.com

ISBN 978-1-0369-0213-1

Typesetting and origination by Inkfish Press.
Printed in the United Kingdom.

CONTENTS

INTRODUCTION

ON THE rocks at Carne, flotsam washes in alongside memories of lost love. A family picnic at Lostwithiel leads to the rediscovery of ancient Cornish language stories. In The Three Ferrets at St Ives, a weary barmaid dreams of sailing away on a yacht with a dubious stranger, and a man in search of love is tricked by the Queen of Fey at Rough Tor.

This captivating anthology showcases exciting contemporary writers, both established and emerging, including Rebecca Johnson Bista, Anastasia Gammon, Tim Hannigan, Kate Horsley, Clare Howdle, Adrian Markle, Tim Martindale, P. T. McAllister, Rob Magnuson Smith, Mark Plummer, Katherine Stansfield, Jackie Taylor, Karen Taylor, Shelley Trower, Emma Timpany, Tom Vowler, Ella Walsworth-Bell, Elaine Ruth White and Becky Wildman. Most were born in Cornwall or live there now; many have set their short story or non-fiction piece within the Cornish landscape, celebrating a love of Cornish history and wildlife. Moving through time and space with each story, you'll enjoy contemporary retellings of folklore, compelling memoirs, and flash fictions that brim with tension and discovery.

This anthology grew out of the magazine we coedit, *Inkfish*. In founding *Inkfish*, we hoped to create a distinctive and friendly online space for textual and visual art, featuring both new and familiar talent. We love great short fiction, poetry, and art, especially those pieces that take us somewhere unexpected. Following our call-out to writers and artists with a connection to Cornwall, we discovered a range of new short stories and non-fiction that made Cornwall feel fresh and unexpected; writing that engages with folklore, history, and landscape in an emotionally compelling way. We always welcome bold experiments with form, and it was a pleasure to see so many strong voices weaving together.

With so many of the writers collected here living near to each other – Penzance and Marazion, Bodmin and Zennor, Hayle, Fowey, Falmouth and St Ives – there was an especially lovely and supportive energy to compiling this anthology. Many of the contributors to this volume knew each other well already. They were in writing groups, or involved with the Penzance Litfest, or had studied together. Others are discovering each other's writing afresh. Making contact with these writers was a particularly rewarding experience. Writing can feel lonely, so books like this help reinforce a sense of community. The central idea for the project gave us all the opportunity to discover something new about our common theme. Reading each other's work, we were able to find both familiar pieces of landscape and surprising resonances. Through each other's words, we saw the Cornish landscape with fresh eyes. Now we present it to you, the reader, to experience this same feeling.

For our cover, we were lucky to find an artist whose work is rooted in the Cornish landscape. Mark Holman's creative practice draws on parallel lives as a horticulturalist and visual artist. His beautiful ink drawing of a foxglove growing on the coast of Marazion reflects his work on sustainability and the entanglement of humans and plants within the environment. This cover image possesses a deep resonance with the pieces gathered here, many of which explore the delicate relationships between people and nature, local history and future possibility, the Cornish landscape that's historical and the one we imagine.

Kate Horsley and P. T. McAllister
Cornwall, 2024

THE CHRISTMAS PARTY

Anastasia Gammon

THE AFTERNOON'S snow was already turning to slush when Lizzy finally managed to escape the party.

Drunken carol singing and the clinking of glasses crept around the edges of the pub's front door, but the sounds were quickly chased away by icy wind. Lizzy zipped up her fleece, her breath clouding in front of her. It was a relief to be free of the suffocating merriment inside, but she wished she'd grabbed a coat before sneaking out.

Hands shoved deep into the pockets of her jeans, Lizzy looked up and was startled to see her best friend, Nora, sitting in the snow atop one of the wooden tables in the pub's courtyard.

'Nora?' A shiver ran up Lizzy's spine, which had nothing to do with the cold night. 'Is that you?'

'Obviously.' Nora jumped down from the table, her trainers making no noise on the snow-covered flagstones. 'Did you think I'd miss your mum's Christmas party?'

'Well… yes.' Lizzy remembered the squeal of the car breaking too late, the black dress and smart, flat shoes shoved to the back of her wardrobe, the broken look on Nora's mum's face as the coffin was lowered into the ground. She shook the images out of her head. 'You're dead. You died months ago.'

It felt like one of them ought to mention it.

Nora rolled her eyes. 'Like I'd let that keep me away.'

It was the eye roll that did it.

Lizzy rushed forward. Immediate, stinging tears blurred her vision.

'It is you.' Lizzy reached out but Nora moved away. Lizzy's fingers closed on cold air.

'Are we going for a walk?' Nora asked. She forged ahead into the open moorland without waiting for an answer.

Wet grass squelched beneath Lizzy's feet, quickly soaking through the thin canvas of her trainers, but still she followed Nora, doing her best to keep up with her friend's confident stride.

She didn't understand how Nora could be here. She didn't care. All that mattered was that her friend was back and that she didn't let Nora out of her sight.

Nora looked exactly as she had the last time Lizzy had seen her. Her golden hair was pulled back in a low ponytail. She was wearing the same ripped jeans and oversized t-shirt, too cold for this late December night. When Nora turned to check that Lizzy was still following, she wore the same pink lip-gloss smile Lizzy knew so well.

'What?' Nora asked when they had walked far enough away from the pub that the wind howled louder than the guests. 'Why are you staring at me?'

'I missed you so much.' Lizzy's words struggled to find their way out.

Nora shrugged. 'Well, I'm here now,' she said, as though she had just been away for a weekend, as though Lizzy was being silly.

'But how?' Lizzy asked.

Nora raised her hands high above her head. 'It's a Christmas miracle,' she shouted up at the wide, starry sky. Lizzy laughed like she hadn't in months. 'Come on.' The girls ran through the snow together.

Up ahead, the old engine house, where Lizzy and Nora had shared so many Cornish pasties and giggly afternoons, loomed against the skyline, but Nora didn't head towards it as Lizzy expected. Instead, she veered off to the left, towards a wire fence that bordered an open mineshaft.

Lizzy stopped.

The ground over the mine shaft had collapsed years ago. Lizzy's mum had always told her not to go near it but there wasn't a child or teenager in the village who hadn't leant over the fence to try to see the bottom, throwing stones and secrets into the dark pit.

Except Nora.

Nora had seen the mine shaft collapse. She had appeared on the local news, clutching her dad's hand while he told the reporter what it had been like to watch the earth split open right in front of them. All Nora had ever said about it was that it had been scary. She had never gone near the mine shaft again.

Now, without hesitation, Nora climbed over the rusted wire fence.

'What are you doing?' Lizzy asked, reaching out to pull Nora back, away from the great hole.

Something stopped her hand before she could touch Nora's pale, bare arm. It wasn't Nora moving away that stopped her this time but a feeling, a prickling on the back of Lizzy's neck, which told her to run back to the pub full of people and lock the doors behind her.

Lizzy gripped the fence next to Nora.

'It's fine.' Nora held out a hand to Lizzy. 'Come on.'

All their lives, Lizzy had followed Nora. She had almost followed her into the road that day in June.

Sometimes, in the middle of the night, when she couldn't sleep for the ache in her chest and the memories in her head, she almost wished she had.

Now, she looked down at the dark, vast hole in the earth. The wire fence dug into the flesh of her palms.

When Lizzy looked back up, Nora's smile was so bright that her teeth seemed to glow in the moonlight, and so what if that smile was a little wider than usual, if she could see a few more teeth? It was Nora. Her best friend back from the dead.

A Christmas miracle.

Lizzy reached for Nora's hand, just like she always did. At last, their fingers made contact, Nora's icy hand wrapping comfortingly around Lizzy's, soothing the stabbing ache from where she had gripped the fence so tightly.

'Lizzy?' a voice called, somewhere far away.

Nora's smile turned into a frown. Lizzy tried to turn around, to see who was calling her, but Nora pulled her forward, slamming her body into the fence. The old wire dug in painfully, straining against her torso.

'Come with me,' Nora said but it didn't sound like Nora's voice at all anymore.

'Lizzy?' the far away voice called again. 'Is that you?'

Lizzy tried to pull back her hand, but Nora's grip

'Without a coat, in December?' Hannah asked. 'Is the party that bad?'

'Yes.' Lizzy curled towards the warmth of Hannah's body. Hannah extricated her arm and wrapped it around Lizzy's shoulders instead.

'Well, I'm here now,' Hannah said. Lizzy had a strange feeling she had heard that before this evening, though she couldn't think where. 'We'll sort your hand and then we can sneak upstairs and have our own party. Like we used to do with Nora,' she added, her voice softening at the mention of their friend. 'How does that sound?'

Lizzy nodded. 'That sounds nice.' They could remember Nora together.

It might almost feel like she was there with them.

THE LAST LONELY PERSON ON TUNA STREET

Becky Wildman

A FEW days ago, I was walking alone along Tuna Street, and there, rising towards me like a tsunami of land, was the ground. Not the ground beneath my feet, the ground about twenty steps in front of me. Tipping up on itself like the world was a piece of paper, folding away. The grey of the pavement, with lines of houses either side, the green wheelie bins, a red car on the road, all rising. It collected into this huge object in front of me, not made up of its individual parts anymore but one threatening mass. The sky bent down behind me out of view, and I was just a word on the page, smashing into another word from the other side.

I had just then been thinking that if I were a

character, if I could choose who I was, then I would just stop feeling. All the little cries inside my head would go away, and I would be in a world of my own, you know, like everyone else, not caring about stuff. If I wanted to be beautiful or brave that wouldn't make it true. You can't just make up who you are. But wanting to not care anymore, could that be true? Maybe I could change the way I thought if I thought about it enough. I wondered if everyone else must want to not care or if they ever even considered it.

Of course, we could all be lying to each other in some universal conscious conspiracy. How do I know I don't feel like everyone else if I don't know how everyone else feels?

I guess I just know. After the ground folded in on me, I reappeared on the other side of the page, and I was thinking, is fighting to fall asleep harder than fighting to stay awake? I decided falling to sleep is harder, I can always stay awake. But I don't know why. Surely the dream is the desired state, where nothing matters because it's all inside your head.

Anyway, I walked on Tuna Street and back to my room on Capelin Field. I'm sure I heard once, somewhere, that they used to be called Morrab Road and North Parade. I don't know when the names changed. In my mind, some tidal wave had turned all the streets into migrating fish, using some mystery of nature to find their way back to the exact spot they were hatched. I think they use taste or smell. Or they listen to the earth's magnetic field in ways we don't understand. When I arrived home, to Capelin Field or North Parade or whatever you call it, I realised I didn't know how I'd got there. I'd just followed my feet without thinking. Perhaps that's what the fish do.

No one was home. I had locked my door to keep the kid inside, which, as you know, is an unusual thing to do, so I made sure no one was around as I found the key to unlock it. Most rooms don't even have keys anymore, they have been lost or forgotten about. I guess since nobody has any wealth or possessions that are not freely available to everyone else, it's not necessary to lock things away. We earn our credits during givetime and can have whatever we want during metime. I was three days into a period of eighty-eight days of givetime. A refuse collector. I'd done it before and didn't really mind the mess. It was kind of helpful in a way that no one's life depended on. Since I was fourteen and it became mandatory, I have been in twenty-four periods of givetime. I've been a hairdresser, a carer for the elderly, a telephone operator for the national grid, a machine operative in a cider packing factory, a taxi driver, an electrician, an optician, an administrator for the distribution of accommodation. All sorts of stuff. Like everyone else.

I just watch the instructional video on day one and then give time to it.

But, anyway, I was lucky my new room still had its key, so that the kid couldn't escape. I unlocked my door and opened it, with a big smile and friendly hello, all exaggerated like you do for kids. He was sitting in the far corner, didn't look up or acknowledge my entrance or anything, which was not unusual.

'What you got there?' I said as I crossed the room. He had unthreaded the carpet at its edge and was running his fingers along the separated fibres.

'Wow look at that.'

I knelt beside him, and he turned. He didn't look at me but back towards the bed. I waved a hand before his eyes which stayed perfectly still, like he didn't see the world at all. In this slow, almost mechanical movement which he has, he picked up his arms and squeezed them around my neck. My heart whispered something to me, and I wrapped him up tightly, forgetting what amount of time passed, holding onto him. And that's what people just don't do anymore. Whether they don't hear those whispers or they don't have them, I don't know. But I read about it once and it used to be a thing. It was called love.

Later that evening, when I walked into the communal kitchen, I thought I saw a sort of black fuzz across the window and the table. The kind that appears when the signal is failing. Like something wasn't quite connecting properly.

Jake was stirring his tea in slow little movements, staring into the whirlpool with blank eyes.

'Hey.' I crossed the kitchen and opened the fridge.

'Oh hey.' He looked up at me from the dream in his cup. 'How's your givetime going?'

I knew that by asking me, what he really wanted was to tell me about his own givetime. He has no interest outside his own head. So, I gave him some mandatory response that allowed him to just keep talking.

'Did I tell you I'm a doctor now? It's pretty unbelievable. Like, last time I was a cashier! Can you believe that?'

He didn't wait for my response. 'So, I'm a gastro surgeon and yesterday I actually cut out a gut! Well, just a section of it, you know, the part that was infected. But can you imagine how that felt for me? Seeing all that mass so intense and so red and just cutting it. I was thinking as I was doing it, *this is going to be really weird for me*, but I just did it anyway. Can you believe that!'

'Is the person ok?'

His face was alive with his own sense of excitement, his projection of himself. He was watching a movie inside his head where he was the star, and he was thinking what a great movie it was.

'I always back myself. Like, he was just this thing, just body parts, but you can't really see the face, the eyes are all taped up and there's a tube down the throat. It was just me and the gut.' He held out his hands in front of him, to demonstrate where the gut was.

'Did he survive? The guy?'

'What? Oh, the guy. I have no idea.' He removed the teabag from his cup and tossed it into the bin.

'I'm doing waste removal.'

'What? Oh yeah, this is a big one for me. Like, I knew someone who was a doctor before, but until you actually see it – I feel like – it's going to change me, you know, give me a greater perspective on the human body, like I've seen the inside of it.'

'Oh yeah, no, I'm sure you'll do a great job.'

'What?' He searched my face for something, like he was looking for a word in a wordsearch, lines of letters that made no sense to him, so he gave up and said, 'bet you're glad to be rid of that kid now you're in givetime.'

'Yeah. Well. He was OK.'

'Yeah, he was quiet at least, a bit odd though.'

'Yeah.' I thought all the kids were getting quieter.

'Do you want to hook up? I've got to be in the hospital for six, but we could do an hour or so if you put some lipstick on?' He was stupidly good looking.

'No thanks.'

'Ok, see you later.' He left the kitchen with his tea and a little smirk on his face like he was really impressed with his tea making. I mean, I was glad he didn't suspect I had kept the kid. I guess he didn't have enough interest in it to suspect anything. But all I could think about was the guy with his gut cut away. Where was he now? This slab of a man was just a story for Jake to tell, he was nothing but fiction. Sometimes I think we are all just stories to each other. And that's why I couldn't give up the kid, even though you're not supposed to keep them in givetime. Because I didn't want him to be a story from the past, I wanted to have him with me and watch the things he was doing and make him laugh and stuff. I know it's stupid.

That night, the kid and I had eaten bread and butter and giggled at the tiny pictures we made from the crumbs. He was sleeping in that innocent way kids do, by my side on our single bed. His mouth was open, and I could hear his breath collapse on itself in the dim light of the night lamp. His ears stuck out and I stroked his hair behind them. I thought about how there was something sweet about his little ears, especially from behind. It made him look real. Like he was this real little person with sticky out ears or something. He didn't look like Malcolm, not at all really. Malcolm had the kid when I met him, but I don't know where he got him from.

Whenever I thought about Malcolm I got a cold chill, like the air of a silent night was running right through me, and I was just a passage to nowhere. I wasn't angry. How could I be? When he met Trisha, who was more beautiful and experienced than me, they'd asked if I wanted to stay on. Lots of people have multiple partners, using each to satisfy different aspects of themselves. It's healthy during metime to prioritise mental health through the achievement of pleasure. And coupling up was never about being exclusive. I wished I could have stayed. But when I saw her touching him, exciting him, it made me feel sick. My stomach would just roll over and over, a lost ball bounding down a never-ending hill. I didn't even know why at first. I'd go on long walks with the kid along the promenade. Watching the cold ocean churn on the sand, holding the grains in its mass then throwing them away again. Birds dotted about like confetti thrown over it, in some sort of tiny celebration of the oceans continued ambiguity. I'd think 'why can't I be normal?'.

One day, after a long walk where I'd tried to let the wind blow away my thoughts and carry them over the sea, me and the kid went back to our rooms, all red faced and fresh. We entered the lounge and were hit by the thick air of desire, heavy in the room like it had its own crushing presence. Trisha and Malcolm were curled together on the sofa, limbs mingling with one another.

'Join us.' A long, reaching arm. Stomach bile in my mouth.

'Erk. She's still got that kid. I thought we were getting rid of it?' Trisha stroked Malcolm's mouth; his lips reached for her finger.

'We could.' His eyebrows raised and he looked at me from inside his own anticipation of pleasure. I had a little picture in my head of when it was just me, Malcolm and the kid, and the kid was laughing, and I was smiling at Malcolm, and he seemed to know everything there was.

'I feel like we've had him long enough, let's just enjoy each other a while.' The long arm outstretched towards me again.

'I'll take him.' I couldn't look them in the eyes. I left the room with the kid, put everything I owned in a backpack and never went back. As we left the house, I heard the shrieks of Trisha's pleasure. And I knew. I knew I was different. He would never think about me other than as a story. But I thought about him as a place. A place inside me.

I watched the kid sleeping and thought about Malcolm. Then I scrubbed the thought away as if it

people were just characters in their story. Years later, I came across the woman that watched me and asked if she still knew Sean.

'What? Oh no, he's dead.'

I cried for a week, and everyone thought there was something wrong with me and tried to give me tablets and stuff. I told them I was fine and decided never to think about Sean, or his lack of being. I put it all in a box and moved to a new room. But that box was there, inside the kid's cry.

When I fell out the other side of the cry, I bent down and took hold of the kid's shoulders. I looked into his eyes. 'You're like me,' I told him. He looked back at me for the briefest of moments before his eyes did this crazy flicking thing they do, like he's in a fast car trying to focus on something out of the window and it keeps moving away. Maybe he was trying to make sense of the world, but it's just a stream of colours with nothing to focus on. I tried to follow the flicker, but it moved too fast. 'You are like me, aren't you?'. He moved away from me and started to touch the wall at the end of the bed where the paint was peeling away. He picked at it, revealing the plaster underneath. I kissed him on the top of the head before leaving the room and locking the door. I'm sure I locked the door.

Then, after twelve hours at work, I was walking alone along Tuna Street on my way home, and everything was quiet; the end of the world quiet. I looked at the rows of houses and tried to imagine the people inside. Beating hearts and inflating lungs, sending impulses down their spinal cords to cook their evening meals. Touching things. Looking at other people and processing what they saw. I wondered if red was red for everyone. Like, how would we know if when someone else saw red, they really saw blue. And all the things that were red in the world, in their head were blue, but that was normal. How could I ask them if their red was really blue? I could try to describe the colour, like its hot and intense. But to them blue would be hot and intense, because all the things that were red to me had always been blue to them. And all the things I think about red, they thought about blue.

The quietness seemed to break, and I could hear my feet on the ground and my breath hitting the air, like I had just woken up. A door on the left-hand side of the street, about three doors ahead of me, opened. I had this feeling of anticipation; some demon was going to come out of that door, and I would have to run.

I looked up and down Tuna Street and I felt there were eyes watching me and watching the door. Some huge invisible eyes that were curious as to what was going to happen. They were pushing me. I listened and thought I could hear a ticking sound. A tick that's trying to track time but has lost count. You know that phrase, 'lose track of time', I always wondered what that meant. Like time was a track you could fall off, and where would you be? I looked back at the open door and the tick became my heartbeat.

And then I thought about these curtains I used to have with flowers on them. And how sometimes, late at night, they didn't look like flowers, they looked like heads. They were all just crammed together on stalks, fighting each other for space. And I used to think if I opened the curtains, there would be a face in the window too. Behind all these struggles in the curtains, it would just be there, like the other side of the veil. Lonely.

But it wasn't a demon who came out the door. Or a face behind the curtains. It was Malcolm. He was smiling and touching a woman that was not Trisha.

'Hiya,' he flicked his eyebrows towards me as they walked past. He had no idea that I was thinking about red and blue and the end of the world and some curtains I used to have. I don't think he even recognised me at all.

I thought my feet were stuck to the ground, but I managed to free them by running. I just started running as if there was some imaginary finish line that I had to make it to. If I stayed where I was nothing would happen, and the story would never be over.

And I thought I must get back to the kid and tell him what love is. And I didn't care about my givetime, I would break the rules because I didn't want to lock him away. I turned onto Capenlin Field and that's when I saw all the police cars and people standing around.

'What's happened?' I asked someone in the crowd.

'A kid's been run over, I think. They say no one was watching him.'

I wasn't different after all. I had only thought about myself. And the ground started to fold up again, like the page. This time it was from behind me so I couldn't see it, but I knew it would close and what would be.

BUT MAN MUST RAISE THE SAIL

Mark Plummer

THERE WAS nothing but sea all the way from here to America. The water just kept going and going, aggressive in its vastness. She watched the waves breaking on the shoreline. Even the small ones curled like snarling lips. One or two children still jumped and screamed happily in the shallows. Their parents were nearby and watching. She used to come here as a child too, after school or at the weekends after Dad had seen the races. They weren't allowed in the sea though. The day would always end with Mum screaming at her or at her brother and the walk home was made longer by the stinging shape of Dad's hand on their thighs.

Two swimmers were out in it. They bobbed around near the buoys easy as bath toys. She wished she had learned. Silly, really, to live her whole life by the sea and not be able to swim. The water was far out – the tide low – now though. She didn't need to worry about it for a while.

It was getting late. The beach was clear of windbreaks and deckchairs and pop-up tents, but a few blankets still held cuddling couples or families with fish and chips. Most people had already climbed the steps where exhausted-looking wetsuits hung on the railings and children had their feet rubbed raw as parents towelled the sand off. At the foot of the steps, flip-flops and plastic buckets full of mussel shells, razor clams and seaweed waited to be forgotten. A breeze ruffled the umbrellas on the picnic tables in front of the takeaway.

'God provides the wind,' her mother always said. 'But man must raise the sail.' Julie never understood what she was going on about. Her mum never let them in the sea but then kept banging on about sails.

Julie looked at the clock. She was behind schedule. She was usually mopping by now. She was late. Always lost in daydreams, her mother would say. The wooden boards advertising ice creams, deckchairs and pasties had to be collected from the path along the top of the beach. The boards were too big for her to carry really and bashed her legs as she walked with them, but she'd gotten used to it now, bruises flowering perpetually but painlessly on her shins. She folded down the umbrellas from the picnic benches then leant them up inside the door ready to go back out first thing in the morning.

'Alright, Jules?'

She turned to see Batesy stumble in through the side door knocking over a stack of empty boxes.

'Blimey, is it that time already? Everything's to pot today.'

'Got my burger, Jules?'

'Not yet. I'll have to cook it.'

She gestured at where his shoes had scattered sand across the floor. 'Bloody hell, Batesy. I'll have to clean all that up.'

He giggled and looked around the kitchen as though trying to focus in on her. His eyes were wide and bloodshot.

'It's alright, Jules. I ain't bothered. You don't need to clean up just for me. Can I have a burger? Cheeseburger, please. I'm starving.'

'Alright. Alright. I'm doing it.'

He giggled again. 'I went down The Ferrets last night.'

'I know I was there.'

'Right, course. Good, weren't it?'

She waited to see if he was being tender or ironic, but there was neither in his eyes. It was just said out of habit.

'Same as every night,' she said. 'Surprised you can remember any of it, the state you were in.'

'That's how I know it was good. I was completely wasted.'

She leant on the counter, the sweet words and promises of last night lost once again in a fog of weed and hangovers.

'Can I have a burger, Jules?'

'I'm cooking it now. Christ, that's three times you've asked me.'

Julie flipped the burger and balanced salad in a bun. Batesy picked up the serrated knife and started carving nicks out of the chopping board.

'Leave that alone. I'll get in trouble for that. I'm fed up with paying for your messes.'

'Sorry, Jules. You'll come down The Ferrets tonight, won't you?'

'I expect so,' she said coquettishly like the women on TV did. 'We'll have to see.' She couldn't help smiling at the idea that they might miss her if she wasn't there.

'It's bloody hot in here, Jules. I'm spinning out because of it. What the fuck are all them knives for?'

'Chopping up vegetables and that.'

'Right, yeah. Could you cook me a burger please, Jules?'

'Alright. Bloody hell. Repeating all the time. You're

off your face, you are. Here, have it.'

'Thanks. You're an angel.' He winked at her, and she felt her cheeks burn. 'See you in the Ferrets tonight: usual time.'

Julie checked her watch – she was behind again – then pulled down the shutters and set the coffee machine to run through its cleaning cycle. Every day, she checked the dates of the milk and wrote Roger a list of what needed to be ordered. He ordered it when he came down to collect the takings early in the morning. Julie cashed up the till. She'd definitely done it wrong. She always did. She was no good with money. Roger would be waiting for her in the morning and have a go at her.

The coffee machine had finished its cycle, so she washed the milk frothing jug and the ice-cream scoops. She'd washed the sandwich knives and chip scoop earlier but had left them on the draining board to remind her to check the fryers were off. They were. And the coffee machine. And the till. And the display cabinets. All off. She checked the fryer again just in case. Julie knotted the bin bag and dropped it outside the back door then she sprayed and wiped down the preparation areas. She swept around then went back to check the coffee machine was off and the freezers were still on then mopped through. She liked seeing the little circles of clean water spread across the floor as she went. Julie went back again to check she had turned off the coffee machine – she had – then had to re-mop over her footprints on the wet floor.

She felt dizzy from the smell of the disinfectant and the heat of the place with the shutters closed, but she liked the claustrophobic feel of it: how safe and cocooned she felt shut away from the roar of the sea. When she opened the back door, a cool breeze rushed in. She emptied the mop bucket into the sink and watched it circle away down the plughole until just the suds and a few veg peelings were left. She pulled them out with her fingers and chucked them in the bin.

Julie set the alarm and – while it bleeped monotonously away – she double-checked the dials on the fryer were off and went out. She locked the door and checked the handle three times, putting her weight behind her hip and pushing it to make doubly sure. She posted the keys into the little box for Roger to collect in the morning.

She left her bag on one of the picnic benches in front of the takeaway and leant on the table for a moment. There were three metal detectorists in different places across the beach. Standing between her and the low sun, their silhouettes looked like vultures. They came every day to pick over what was left behind while the seagulls did their final check of the bins. Julie imagined finding buried treasure on the beach and wondered what she'd do with it. She could travel, go on a plane, cuddle someone on a blanket on a foreign beach. Or buy her own place. She'd probably keep working, she supposed. It was good to keep a routine. There was nothing else to do anyway.

An old man was walking slowly across the top of the beach with a stick. Children kicked a football and chased it. A group of teenagers came down the steps with disposable barbeques and bottles clinking together in carrier bags. It would be too cold in the evenings to do that soon. The seasons were changing. Everything was always changing. The customers in the takeaway would soon change from sunburnt English tourists to the autumnal Germans and Japanese coach trippers. After that came the coughing dog walkers and old women in wetsuits. Not old at all, she corrected herself. She went to school with some of them. Middle-aged at most. There'd be them and there'd be children in wellies and Eskimo suits with little fur-lined hoods and red cheeks and runny noses that needed wiping and a nice hot chocolate to warm them up. Her working days would be shorter as it got quieter, and she'd need to spend more time at home with Mum and Dad anyway. They couldn't afford the carers or meals on wheels in the winter with the heating, so she needed to help look after them.

The grates still needed to go up over the windows that didn't have shutters. Julie dragged them round to the front and lifted the first one up to the window but missed the hooks they sat on and had to put it back down again.

'Can I help?'

The old man she'd seen walking across the beach was standing behind her, though he wasn't as old as she'd thought from a distance. No older than her father, probably younger. And the walking stick was more like a cane than an old man's stick.

He took the opposite end of the grate from her and smiled while Julie counted to three then lifted. The man didn't lift though and instead looked a little surprised. Eventually, he gripped his cane between his knees and then lifted his end. With the stick between his legs, he moved forwards in jerks and the grate rattled against the window's wooden frame. Julie hooked her end into place then went down to help get his side in. She could see two places where the grate had scuffed the white paint revealing the blue it had been painted a few years before. Roger would go mad when he saw it. She'd always preferred the blue really. Still, at least he hadn't smashed the glass or anything.

'Can I help you with the other one?'

He had a slight accent. He sounded like someone from one of the old films.

'Oh, it's alright. Thank you all the same. We're

meant to do it on our own really. Insurance or something.' It was a lie, but a pretty good one she thought. Might well be true.

She lifted the second grate into place and put the padlocks onto both. The man was still there watching her. He smiled and leaned on his cane.

'All done for the day?'

'Afraid so. Did you want to buy something? I'm afraid everything's locked up now.'

'My name's Christopher,' he said and held out his hand.

'Julie,' Julie said. She thought of the crap from the sink and how she hadn't even washed her hands afterwards, just wiped them on her apron. The same hand he was now holding and could probably smell.

'I was just—' he pulled a bottle of wine from the canvas bag over his shoulder. 'I was just going to sit and have a glass of wine and enjoy the evening. Would you like to join me?'

The man looked smart in his blazer and shirt. His trousers were clean, and the front seam was straight and crisp. His cane and the cotton flat cap he wore looked expensive, but his shoes were tatty, and his teeth were stained and crooked. She tried to think of an excuse. She usually went to The Ferrets in the evening.

'You've no idea how happy it would make me,' he said.

'Well, okay. One drink.'

'Wonderful,' the man said and started towards one of the benches. 'Oh,' he said and came back to her. 'I haven't got any glasses. Can you get some from the takeaway?'

'No. Sorry, no I can't.'

'They surely won't miss two paper cups?'

'It isn't that. It's all locked now.'

'Don't you have a key?'

'I've posted them in the box. I've got to put them in there and then Roger picks them up early in the morning when he collects the takings.'

'They leave the money in there all night? That's very trusting of them.'

'Not really,' she said. 'This place is like Fort Knox.'

He rattled the grating and nodded. 'So, no cups then.'

'I'm happy to drink from the bottle if you are,' she said.

His face brightened and they sat at a picnic table. Christopher made a show of opening of the bottle; flicking up the cuffs of his blazer before cracking the screw top open. He passed the bottle to her with the label against his sleeve like waiters do on TV. Julie took a drink and passed it back to him.

'Are you here on holiday?'

He licked his lip and pushed the bottle back to her.

'In a way. I'm just here for the day.'

'Day trip.'

'I suppose. Many people would say my whole life is a holiday.'

'Retired?'

He laughed. But he didn't seem to be laughing at her like them in the pub did. This was the kind, warm laugh that friends, fathers and lovers gave in the soaps her parents watched.

'No, no, not retired. I'm not quite that old. Did you see the yacht that arrived in the bay this morning?'

'A woman here earlier said it belonged to a film star.'

'Not quite. It's not as grand as all that, but I find it comfortable.'

'Oh, that must be lovely.'

'I sail up and down the coast and see some of the most beautiful places in the world,' he said.

She tried to imagine it. Every day a different place. Staying in the best ones. Leaving the bad ones before you had time to settle. He was watching her, his head tilted to one side and smiling quizzically, like someone pouring water into a bath and waiting to see when it will overflow the top.

'Have you ever been to Biarritz?'

'No.' She shook her head and could feel the water brimming the top, hovering over the edges ready to pour out.

'It's really stunning. Amazing. Still, I'm not sure I've been anywhere quite like here.'

The plug had suddenly been pulled out again. The water was draining away.

'Yes,' she said. 'My mum always says: why travel when you got this on your doorstep.'

'Very wise. Still, you must get bored in the winter.'

'I suppose so. But my mum and dad are elderly and sick. They need looking after so that uses up time.'

He nodded and lifted the bottle that was still in her hand gently to her mouth.

'I expect that the season will end soon, and the town will be lifeless. Then the autumn storms will be rolling in before long,' he said.

She noticed raindrops hitting and soaking into the wood of the table then felt them on her bare arms and face.

'What a shame we can't get one of the parasols out from in there,' Christopher said. 'There's no secret way in? Oh well. Come along, drink up.'

The wine didn't seem to be going down very much at all. She felt like she'd drunk more on her own than was gone from the bottle. The old man's hand brushed past her knee under the table, and she flinched. He looked at her questioningly.

'Are you alright, my dear?'

Maybe he had just been looking for his cane.

Someone with a movie star lifestyle like this wouldn't be interested in someone like her.

It was getting dark now; the rain had let the evening slip in early. The sand shivered under the growing breeze.

'I suppose you're closing for the season soon?'

'No, we're open all year. We get customers all the time. Older people' – she hesitated over the words – 'older people start coming now on coach trips then we get busy again at half-term and Bonfire Night and around New Year.'

'It must be pretty miserable here in the winter.'

It was, she supposed.

'I couldn't bear the cold,' he said. 'English winters are too cold for me. I always take the yacht down to the Med over winter; the Mediterranean.'

Julie shivered, the cold suddenly grasping her shoulders. She thought of Batesy and the others up at The Ferrets. She'd usually be there by now. It would be loud and stink of piss with sticky carpets and flat beer and the people in there were all scabs and druggies and drunks and she knew they took advantage of her, but they would all be wondering where she was, and the place was warm. She rubbed her hands over the goose bumps on her bare arms.

Christopher took off his jacket and wrapped it around her. He left his arm across her back, his hand rubbing her arm. Every few rubs, his fingers would reach further round towards her breast, but he didn't react when she looked at him. Perhaps he didn't realise. She'd feel guilty having to turn him down after he'd been so nice. Batesy and the others would have a good laugh about it when she told them: an old man feeling her up.

'Here,' he said and pulled another bottle from his bag. 'Another round! Drink up. It will keep you warm.'

He wasn't so old really. Anyway, men didn't age like women. She'd read a thing on Facebook about a man who had a baby when he was ninety-two. It was quite common really.

'What's the Mediterranean like?'

'Oh, wonderful. You'd love it.'

'I've never even been out the country.'

'You'd love it, the air actually tastes metallic with all the golden light in it.'

He spoke like someone off of the TV. His hand worked down lower to hold her far hip.

She pictured herself sunbathing on the deck of a yacht with glistening, calm water around her. She would be in a white bikini with bronzed skin and her stomach would be flattened by not being surrounded by chips all day long. Her skin would be cleared by being out of the fryer grease and in the sunshine. She imagined parties with champagne and cocktails, waiters in white suits and black bow ties, guests commenting on her style and elegance.

The rain started to get heavier. It worried the surface of the incoming sea, hiding the currents and blurring the outlines of the now submerged rocks.

'Perhaps we should shelter under the awnings,' he said.

He took her hand and led her to the patch of decking under the ice cream hatch that was dry. She looked at her hand in his, sheltered and warm. There were splits in her knuckles from bleach, the nails misshaped, and the fingertips swollen from biting. Christopher's hands were tough but tanned and well-kept. The backs weren't wrinkled or hairy. He couldn't be that old. You can always tell someone's age from their hands. She'd heard that somewhere. She was a little drunk.

He held her close in the small area of shelter. He smelled of aftershave. She liked the familiarity of his pipe tobacco, the same her grandfather had smoked. He kissed her. She let him and within a few seconds opened her mouth for him, tasting his breath and feeling the stubble of his top lip on hers. She could see his eyes rolling back in his head and giggled that she was the one causing such pleasure. He laughed too, pushing that warm breath like a tropical breeze into her mouth. As they parted, his head continued the rolling movement for a second. She imagined herself stepping onto a jetty in Africa and grasping the rope railing before telling the tanned harbour master who'd rushed to help her that she just needed to shake off her sea-legs. She could see his face – foreign, handsome, confused – desiring her. Part of Africa must be in the Mediterranean.

'Come with me.'

'What?'

'Come with me. Come with me tonight to the yacht and then tomorrow we'll head off. We can be in France by tomorrow night, then work our way down to the Med.'

The tide was pushing right up now; shrinking the beach, the whole town, everything. Maybe it would come all the way up and submerge the takeaway, hiding it forever. She saw it rising over the cliffs and the harbour, sinking The Ferrets, washing away Batesy and all of them, the old school, Mum and Dad's, the corner shop, her little bedsit, all of it gone.

'I've never met anyone like you. We've only had these few short hours, but I can't imagine going on without you,' he said and kissed her neck.

'I haven't got a passport. All of my money and clothes and stuff is at home.'

'We can sort all that in the morning.'

'I can't go to the Mediterranean in my work apron.'

'There'll be time for all that in the morning.'

In the corner of the decking was a football that had been left behind. A child somewhere, a little boy, would realise in the morning. They'd sigh or moan or cry and need a kiss on their salty, tear-covered cheek.

'We could have a life of luxury together. Eventually we can have a family.'

'Alright.'

He kissed her again and she watched the waves coming up towards them, waltzing their way up the sand. He collected his bag and cane; it seemed like a ridiculous affectation as he clearly didn't need it and climbed the hill away from the beach easier than she did. He walked with one arm around her hip pulling her close to him. She could feel the change moving in his pocket. The sea rolled unstoppably up the sand behind them, pushing them on their way.

On the dark pathway that looped back over the takeaway and towards the town, he stopped and kissed her. Christopher's hand slid up her ribs and pawed at her breast. Julie smiled. It was just like she thought: he was the same as Batesy and the others. There was no yacht or Mediterranean, just like there was none of the promised tenderness and relationship the day after from Batesy. At least Christopher's promises were better. It was a nice dream to choose for a night. She heard the sea sigh as it reached its highest point and started to roll back out.

'Let's go,' she said.

She looked back over the beach, covered in footprints now; wrinkled and thrown back like a hotel bedsheet. She hadn't taken the bags up to the bins. The seagulls would pull them apart by morning. There'd be rubbish and mess all over the decking. Roger would be livid. Well, she couldn't do anything about it now, she'd just have to clear it up in the morning.

Christopher must have forgotten that he was supposed to be a stranger in the town: he led her, pulling her gently on through the streets. They were heading away from the harbour. She smiled to herself and wondered how he'd explain away the fact they were arriving at a B&B or a dingy flat rather than a yacht. He was quite young, really. Probably no older than Batesy, just that his skin was worn from the sun whereas Batesy was pickled in cider.

'This isn't the way I would normally take to the harbour,' she teased him.

'Well, I don't know the town very well,' he said.

She wondered how long he would keep up the pretense.

He stopped them outside of some flats and kissed her again.

'This doesn't look like a yacht?' she said in faux-innocence and dug him playfully in the ribs.

'What?' he asked and rubbed where she'd hit him.

'Come on.'

He pulled her down an alley at the side of the flats. It was so dark and narrow that she couldn't see anything at all, and just allowed herself to be pulled by him. They twisted around corners that she didn't even see.

Then she heard it.

At the end of the alley in front of them was the sound of waves beating at the promenade. Ocean winds rattled rigging and boats strained on their ropes like vicious dogs. He gripped her hand tighter and lead her onwards like a sail helplessly caught in the wind. One more corner and she saw it, shimmering in the moonlight: that ever-changing, churning, rebirthing sea and the yacht bobbing on it.

ANOTHER PLACE

Jackie Taylor

'THE COUNCIL has given us notice. I tried, but...'
She couldn't continue, and anyway, she had nothing
material to add.

C remained exactly where he was, staring out of
the metal framed window towards the sea. He didn't
ask – so what now, or how long have we got, or even
why. He couldn't ask. It would have been so much
easier for her if they could have had a discussion or
made a plan. But C no longer had the ability to
synthesise speech. A bead of condensation settled on
the aluminium ridge above his cheekbone, and she
wiped it away before it had a chance to fall.

Dusk settled slowly over the rusty garden furniture
scattered across the lawns. A tractor crawled along
their boundary, headlights on, hard-flailing the hedges

and throwing shredded sycamore and hawthorn up into the air. It was early spring, too close to the nesting season really for winter cutting, and she wondered about the beetles and the ladybirds, and how much progress the swallows had made on their journey from Africa.

She'd driven back from the Council office in town too fast, disorientated by patches of fog on the coast road and the sick emptiness that replaced the adrenalin of the meeting. She'd almost missed the iron gates and had to turn in sharply, her wheels spitting gravel. The building, an unlisted Edwardian villa, was unlit. It wore its history on its sleeve; block-built extensions, fire doors, and metal fire escapes revealed its progression from merchant-built family home, through wartime hospital, to old people's home, to hospice, its most recent use. A flimsy lean-to ran the width of the building, still lined with wipe-down wing chairs from the days when patients nodded in the sunshine while their visitors enjoyed the view. As she pulled up in front of the building, she looked up, knowing that C would be waiting where she'd left him, in front of the window, lined up with his brothers.

The Chairman had said, 'Our agreement was for temporary use only. Until due diligence was done and dusted, and finance in place – so next week, no later.'

She'd negotiated two weeks, exaggerating how

much stuff there was to move. She was shown a 3D model of the new development. The words swirled: luxury apartments, penthouse suites, underground garaging, prime location, aspirational, lock-up-and-leave, swimming pool, restaurant, 24-hour concierge. She was given little time to speak.

'Place gives me the creeps,' the Chairman said, walking his fingers through the 3-D model's high security gates and along the artist's impression of a herringbone brick driveway. 'The sooner it's brought back into proper use, the better.'

More water had beaded on C's face, something he'd been prone to since she'd cleaned away the remains of his velvety skin with sugar soap to reveal the sculpted metal beneath. With the perished beige fabric and glue removed, his face held the soft silver glow of moonlight. Stripped of tell-tale skin, a hint of oxidisation beneath the small emergency solar array across his forehead was visible.

'You mustn't be scared,' she whispered. 'I'll be with you, I promise. I'll hold your hand. We'll sing.'

She knew the reality of it; they couldn't carry on like this. She knew that C was existing on stand-by power only. All the main batteries had been removed from the brothers when the hospice closed. But still, there was that final shutdown to face – the recovery of wiring, the sorting, the stripping, the picking over of C's frame. Those final, irreversible steps. He had served. They all had. They deserved more than being dismembered and dumped into a furnace without ceremony or thanks.

C had cared for her husband John in a way that she could not. When she had nothing but left-over love for the man he'd been, when she had nothing to offer but anger and frustration and guilt, C had sat with John. In the early days, he helped John identify birds and record them in his log. Later, C had read to him, picked up the things he dropped, found his glasses, held the beaker to his lips, patiently, gently, lovingly. When she visited, she often found them singing in the sunroom. C provided the soundtrack, identifying tunes based on John's tentative humming. Simon and Garfunkel had been their favourite. She had been so relieved to be so excluded.

For John's final two days, she had sat on one side of the bed, while C sat on the other. She dozed. C stayed alert. C was able to mould his hand to fit exactly over John's, cold steel against burning skin. She would love him forever for that.

Now C was lined up with his brothers, twenty-six of them in total, like tin soldiers, looking out towards the horizon. Would it have been easier if they hadn't been given kind eyes that flashed with joy, or skin that was soft to the touch, or voices that could sing? When the hospice closed, she had moved in to care for them. Twenty-six figures standing in the window to bear witness, to stand as testament, to ask a question about debt and gratitude. None of them had enough power left to move themselves, or to respond to her commands. And now the vigil was over. The Council's contractors would arrive in two weeks.

In one of the outbuildings, she found an old sack trolley. There were steps and terraces to negotiate, but she managed to wheel the first of the brothers out onto the lawn, his head resting over her shoulder. She positioned him, her practice piece, amongst the reeds by the choked-up pond. Over the next days, she placed the rest of the brothers around the gardens amongst the nettles and bramble, the bracken and the gorse. She sat them in rusty metal chairs as if they were about to take tea, on a swing-seat, in the middle of what had been the croquet lawn. Playing its part in the installation, the weather veered between torrential rain and dismal, settled fog. She photographed everything.

She left C until last, arranging and rearranging the brothers and documenting her process until she could put it off no longer. She wheeled him down the drive, her trolley sinking lopsidedly into the uneven gravel, then out of the gates and across to the cliff edge. She wedged him against an outcrop of lichen-covered granite, with tiny shiverings of last season's thrift beside him and the full spread of the sea at his feet.

She sat with him for two days, as he had sat with John at the end, her hand moulded over his, cold skin against cold metal. She hummed hymns from her childhood, and Simon and Garfunkel's greatest hits, and recited shards of poems she'd learned by heart at school. She let the mist and rain settle on him and run in rivulets down his face. She watched gannets dive-bombing, and cormorants slicing like arrows above the waves, and she wondered how much progress the swallows had made on their journey from Africa.

The weather cleared and delivered a faint sunrise with enough energy for a final power down. While she slept, the emergency solar array across C's forehead caught the cool sunlight, and he opened his mouth as if to sing.

VANISHING POINT & LOZENGE

Tom Vowler

VANISHING POINT

AFTER YOUR father ran off with his student and your mum ended herself as Plath had, I called at your flat, marshalled clothes onto you and headed to places I'd slayed my own grief. God's own landscapes, I'd heard them called, terrain the poets and lovers had colonised. Look, I said, what torment can sustain itself in the presence of this? But you just stood there, a skeleton languishing in its own skin. Beauty, I saw, would become your tormentor, so I lured you into the city's underbelly, hinterlands where the marginalised dwelt. We loitered with junkies, the homeless, the sick and the relegated. These glimpses of squalor, however, acted not as cautionary tales, but as lures, as a potential blueprint for you.

I gave up the tenancy on my apartment and moved my belongings into yours, the neighbour who'd smiled so effusively before, now issuing atrophying glares on realising we were a couple of queers. After cradling your body for an entire afternoon, I phoned in sick for you, told your boss you were extremely infectious, lest she send any scouts snooping around. I took control of your finances and within a week you became a marionette, incapable of autonomy, content to relinquish all of life's decisions.

I forked food into you, watched as you let it break down in your mouth before mustering a swallow. Sometimes I'd go heavy on salt or chili, just to illicit a reaction, but you remained impassive, the grief manifest in your body as well as your mind now. I withheld food, sometimes for the whole day, waiting for some corporeal entreaty that never came. I bathed you, raising and lowering limbs in twice-weekly ablutions, tilting your head back to keep the shampoo from your eyes. I read to you at bedtime, texts I thought might undermine your descent, stories to rouse and tantalise.

One Tuesday I drove us through the car wash on acid, our faces pressed to the windows of my Peugeot as mosaics of suds dissolved our egos. My fear that psychedelics could spiral you into a maze of psychosis proved unfounded, and although it never lasted, it was in these times I witnessed flickers of you returning.

I wrote to your father, attempting a reconciliation I didn't think he deserved. He replied with two salvos: 1) that he always suspected you were a lesbian; 2) there would be nothing left in his estate for you.

I first noticed the colour leaching from you after we swam in the sea; not that you moved beyond the swell raising and lowering your body like a buoy. Whereas the blood returned to my own skin on the shore, yours retained its sallowness until I sat you by the radiator at home. I apologised for not feeding you properly, ordered the most vibrant food I could find, until the interior of the fridge resembled a rainbow. But each day you appeared more and more like a grainy photograph, an approximation of yourself. Washing you one night I swear I could see the surface of the bath through you.

This has to stop! I yelled with all the volume I could assemble, and the notes of terror or love in my voice must have broken through, as you looked at me for the first time in a week and nodded.

LOZENGE

FORAGING FOR morels in the woods last week he'd come across a wild boar piglet, the wretched thing perhaps four or five days old, its umbilical cord still attached. He assumed the mother had been shot by a hunter, sensed the animal was hours from death. He looked around for a hunk of wood, something with length so he could distance himself a little from the act. In the end he realised he had neither the mettle to remove its misery, nor the indifference to abandon it. And so he had carried it down to the house, this honey and caramel-striped lozenge, cradling it as one would a baby, the creature with no strength to protest. Inside he found an old crate, in which he laid some blankets and a bowl of water. He attached a cable-tie to the umbilical cord and cut just below it.

He expected to find it dead the following morning, but there was life still there, and so he took the laptop outside and searched for what to do next. A website that rescued young boars listed a milk formula used for lambs and young goats, so he drove to the agricultural store, where he also bought a feeding bottle. An hour later he was sitting in the crate as the animal suckled frantically, one bottle then another, and he wondered how a sow's nipples could withstand such trauma.

He put a tray with some gravel in one corner and got on with the day's tasks. By lunchtime the animal had perked up and seemed calm in his presence, and a day later he cut a hole in the crate so it could come and go, which it did, the clip of its trotters like dainty heels on the flagstones as it shadowed him. To his surprise it took to using the litter tray. The more he hand-fed the animal, the more he realised returning it to the wild would be unfeasible, the absence of fear for humans, for those who would aim a rifle at it. He vowed to build a pen in the field, somewhere hidden from the road as it was illegal to keep a wild creature as a pet.

When the children returned from far-flung universities for the summer, the creature took to following them around the property, grafting itself to the family. He watched as they tried teaching it to fetch a ball, gave up protesting when they fed it from the table. He'd tell them about his diagnosis another time, before they left for their mother's, or when they came for Christmas. For now, it seemed right only to let the laughter reside.

SURVIVAL LESSONS

Katherine Stansfield

FOUR OF them, sometimes five – a dog or a spoiled cousin. Their lives are exquisite yet they long to escape something unnamable that compels them to leave home on the first day of the holidays: *it's a scorcher*, say the boys, and Cook has packed a hamper. As if these are reasons enough for what follows.

The girls must leave a note with full directions and a map of the adventure, with the time Mother and Cook should expect them back. *Just like girls to dally!*

Then off they trot, the boys and the girls plus cousin or dog, and after a jolly good slog it's the girls who want to stop. *Just like girls to nag!*

So, the boys find an island in the last of the light, or map the best way up a mountain before tea, or reach a clearing in the forest's heart that waits for their knapsacks.

The boys now must plan how they'll attack tomorrow, tell the girls to take charge of domestic arrangements so the boys can rest their clever heads. The girls make up beds from bracken – there's always bracken – and moss, just the right amount, to make beds soft for sleeping. And their make-do home for the night? Let's say it's a handy cave with a floor of sand, but it could just as easily be a hollow tree, an abandoned rustic's hut, a caravan of red and gold. The boys' choice will always be the right one, and will always, somehow, be waiting for them just when they need it.

Wherever they are, the girls must sweep the place, their brooms fashioned from twigs left from the firewood supply which the girls gathered quietly, for they mustn't chatter, the boys say, while the boys do the hard work of thinking. And so the girls sweep, and while sweeping they speak in the language they have learned every day of their short lives: wordless, urgent.

Their thinking done, the boys light the fire so the girls can cook the boys' supper. The flames catch as they never fail to for the boys who keep the matches from the girls. *Just like girls to moan!*

And the girls should be busy anyway – there's

supper to find! Born to find berries blindfolded in every wilderness, these girls, and now the boys are sleeping, and when the girls have washed and dried and put away the supper things, and washed and dried and darned the clothes, they agree: they need to leave.

They creep, these girls, to the back of the cave, to the roots of the tree, under the caravan, to the hut's hidden attic, and dig up the knives buried while sweeping. The knives pressed on them by Mother, by Cook, by the women they passed on their way who worried. *Just like girls to be afraid!*

They retrieve the berries they gathered, the poisoned and the safe. They light torches of moss from the fire that must never burn out, never leave them in darkness. Then they're off. They take the cousin or the dog and sweep their prints as they go. *Just like girls to scope the exits!*

THE SMALLEST THINGS

P. T. McAllister

WHEN THE first snow falls, it clears dirt from the air. That's what my grandmother used to say.

'Picks it up on the way down. Filters everything, so it does.' She'd be up first thing; gingham-clad bottom bobbing as she rubbed half a lemon on our windows. 'Stops condensation,' she'd chirp, before reminding us to, 'Never eat snow until at least the second day.'

We'd smile, mouthing her warnings to each other behind her back as we pulled on warm clothes and ran from the cottage she raised us in.

'And even then,' she'd shout from the door, 'you need to make sure you don't scoop too deep.'

It's funny, I don't remember any of us eating

snow. Not ever. So perhaps her advice had the desired effect.

As I trudge from the cottage now, signed papers in hand, rugged vegetation skirts the route to Penzance. The dunes are weighted with a cool frosting that mirrors the crashing waves and a growing band of gold shows the tide is on its way out. I should still make the last post and be able to walk home this same way. When it's revealed, the beach is a golden highway, a ring around St Michael's Mount. I want to soak in every minute of it while I'm still living here.

'Never forage bladderwrack once the tide has turned.' Another questionable gem that makes me laugh as I notice the seaweed shrivelling on the shoreline.

When she died, things changed fast. It stopped snowing each winter. The familiar smell in the cottage of baking, mingled with her perfume and a touch of damp faded. Even the air felt different – cooler, bitter somehow. I cleared her jewellery from the living-room windowsill in a fit of desire to do something, anything; wrongly thought that hiding reminders of her would help us get through. I hadn't considered how the light used to catch the costume jewels, splaying colours over the walls, making it feel like home. Later, I couldn't remember how it was arranged and didn't want to put it back wrong. It felt too painful to try. The others struggled too. Elizabeth cried in her bed for weeks, so I sang to Joel as I rocked him to sleep each night, hoping he wouldn't hear her through the walls.

When the priest came to say we were being split up – me bound for an aunt in Canada, Elizabeth to the workhouse and Joel to the orphanage – I told him no. He laughed.

'I promised to keep everyone together: promised our mother, then later our grandmother,' I said.

'How can a sixteen-year-old support two young 'uns?' he'd sneered.

'Hopefully with your help.'

We never saw him again.

I kept my twice-made promise.

Now, as I think of Elizabeth finishing her nursing training, Joel starting at Bristol and me free to do… anything, a flake of snow falls to the ground before me.

Maybe the new house will birth memories of its own. Maybe it doesn't matter which way her jewellery goes up in the window of a new home.

Maybe what's needed right now is a fall of snow.

SURFACE TENSION

Adrian Markle

MY LEG never healed right after it broke in a tackle, so my friends didn't call me much during the summer when there was sports going on somewhere. But Ricky was always calling every number he'd ever gotten at school to see if anyone wanted to go 'on the water' – whatever that meant. After I'd been inside alone for a couple weeks, I finally said yes one day when the sun flooded down, maybe the first kid from our school to ever do that, to say yes to him.

Before I could cancel, his uncle's pickup was rumbling smoke in front of my house. Ricky leapt from the cab to meet me and kept reaching for my arm like I was an old lady, but I shook him off. I wasn't crippled, and he was the skinniest kid in our year so what help would he really be anyway. I sat crooked in the middle of the bench seat with my bad leg pressing up against Ricky's, the stick-shift hitting my other knee every second gear, and empties rattling against my foot when we took a corner.

I wished I never answered the phone.

Ricky was freckled but the freckles were small and not defined. We used to joke he was just always dirty – when he wasn't around to hear.

He must have noticed that his uncle's cigarette smoke was stinging my eyes because he cranked down the window, arm pumping like a piston.

As we left paved roads behind, long thin pines rose up beside us, and he started pointing things out through 'em. But I never saw anything, and I couldn't catch his words over the wind whipping through the yawning window. The truck peeled off down a series of narrowing dirt paths.

I watched most of the drive in the rear-view mirror. Somewhere back there, my friends were playing football.

His uncle left us on a trail and drove away, dust curling up behind him. Ricky's skin already had a sheen, and he wiped his forehead with the neck of his shirt that had the sleeves ripped off. He grabbed me by the hand and pulled me down toward the water that was glinting diamond sunlight through the trees.

'What do you think?' he asked. 'Don't have the money to build yet, but this is where the cabin will be.' We stood in an empty lot with downed tree trunks dragged into a ring around a pile of half burned logs and charred cans poking out from the ash.

'He coming back, or?' I asked.

Ricky squinted and tucked his arms in tight against his narrow rib cage. 'Come on,' he said and slumped down to the reedy, swampy shore, green film floating.

I limped down behind him. He whipped a crinkling blue tarp off a dented aluminum boat, just bigger than a bathtub.

I looked back to the trail. There wasn't anybody around. His uncle's dust had settled on the road, the engine noise had faded to nothing. All I heard was Ricky's shallow nervous breathing and the little waves lapping at the shore.

'How do you usually fish?' he asked.

'Normal way,' I lied, never having done it at all.

'I've just got these cheap spincasters from the hardware store, but they're good. Good rods. Good for the trout up here, at least.'

He pushed the boat off the pebble beach into the water and stood behind it, ankle deep, waiting for me, his expression wavering. I told myself it'd only be an afternoon. He held it steady while I climbed on. I'd barely stepped in when my leg started shifting under me and I felt myself pitching back. But Ricky's hand wrapped around my arm, thin with no give, like wire, and he stopped me falling.

The boat was dented all over and the mesh benches that stretched across it had holes wearing through.

He shooed me to the front and ripped the cord a few times on the outboard. The engine coughed alive and then sputtered like it was to die again, but it carried us in fits and starts away from the shore, two rods sticking over the edge, cigarette butts rolling across the bottom. I wanted off, to throw myself into the murky water just there where it was still shallow and shuffle back to shore so I wasn't stuck way out on the lake when the engine gave up the ghost.

I took a deep breath and readied myself against the edge of the boat to drop off it. The boat limped a bit to one side under my shifting weight and Ricky tutted and corrected for it. But then the engine smoothed out and suddenly we were going. Really moving. Ricky's face turned calm, janky teeth peeking out through a slow smile. The sun stuck gold to his skin and instead of looking dirty out there, he shone.

I took my hand off the side like that and turned to face forward as the boat bounced over the lake top. The wind washed across my face, and I started to remember how free I'd felt, back when I could run.

THE CORMORAN CAUSEWAY

Kate Horsley

'BIG JUMP now.' Dad wraps his hand around mine and swings me onto the next rock ledge.

The sea's leaping in and the black rocks are slick. My flip-flops skid and I plunge into a shallow pool. Seawater drenches my summer shorts and splashes my face.

'Okay?' Dad's mouth is tight, his face darkening the baby blue August sky. Well, it was blue earlier. Now it's turning purple like the bags under Dad's eyes.

'Great,' I smile at him. I scrabble up, wincing. My palms are waffled pink and white, skinned knees stinging with salt. I bite my lip.

'No tears, Sophie. We're soldiers, remember?' His hand rests on the sunbaked top of my head for a moment and then he's off again, making huge strides over the smooth grey rocks like the giant who built a causeway in that story he told me last summer.

I stare into the rock-pool while he's ahead of me, spot two sea anemones, their tendrils feathery pink in the dark mirror of the water. From behind a green cloud of weed, a shrimp darts, see-through as a glass pipe, the heart beating so clearly inside it. I want to stop properly to see if I can find a hermit crab, or a new species of fish that's never been discovered before.

'Sophie! Come on.'

How did he get so far ahead? I clamber after him in panic. The tide is racing faster now. A wave jumps up on the rocks. It catches me, making my hands, knees, eyes throb, like a little voice inside pinching me hard. *Keep up, Silly, or you'll lose him.*

It's slippery on the rocks and my legs are short. One of my flip-flops loosens and I stop to get a grip on it. The sea lashes my toes. The sky's turning dark. I wonder if it's supposed to be like that.

'Dad!' I need him to stop for a minute so I can catch up. 'Daddy?'

He doesn't turn and I don't know if he's heard me. This morning, I left his pills on the counter for him, blues, pinks and yellows and a note with a smiley face that said, 'Remember to take me! :-)' I didn't see him swallow them though.

Last summer in Mevagissey, he wasn't on the pills. He was always laughing. One day, we went on an adventure to the Lost Gardens of Heligan. On another, we drove to Penzance and rambled along the coast, searching for hidden coves and rocks we could lift to look for starfish. At Pedn Vounder, we saw a massive crab that Dad said was edible, though mainly it just looked sad to be found.

In each place we stopped, we ate a little bit of picnic – raisins or tuna sandwich or apple – and Dad told me stories about the places we'd discovered.

He said you could hear a ghost child laughing through the stream bubbling at Heligan – the little boy liked to walk in green places, so the Spriggans took him. In another story, a sea monster called Morgawr wrapped her long neck around sailing ships at Pendennis Point. My favourite story was about the Cormoran Causeway, where a giant built an island of rocks and stole cows from all the farmers until a boy from Marazion rowed out one night to catch him.

'For all his boldness, the giant fell down the pit Jack dug and couldn't see his way out,' Dad said. 'After he died, Cormoran's heart stayed deep in the well, so angry and sad that it turned to stone.'

I always secretly wanted to find him, the giant, and give him a big hug to make him feel better.

On our final day here last summer, my flip-flop broke, and I slipped between two rocks and cut my knee. Dad's arms came down to where I was and scooped me up.

'Quick, quick,' he said, 'let's get you fixed.' He piggy-backed me all the way back to the beach near our cottage, where Mum was sitting with Ollie asleep on her lap, reading her book.

'Here's a patient who needs urgent treatment,' said Dad. 'Do you have plasters?' While Mum sorted my knee, Dad gave me a hug and kissed the top of my head. 'Have a really good cry,' he whispered. 'I think you'll feel better after this.'

I feel like I'm catching up to him now. Maybe when I do, he'll see how bad my knee and hands are, and he'll scoop me up and tell me it's ok. Though I had a growth spurt before my birthday and I'm too big to carry now. And even if he could carry me, he couldn't carry me back to Mum, probably ever now that she's gone.

I reach the next inlet, but there's still no sign of Dad. My stomach gets heavy and it's harder to breathe. Like that time I got lost in Tesco's and I thought I'd never see them again, Mum and Dad and my little brother Ollie. But then I turned a corner by the Spaghetti Hoops and there they were.

The tide is right in, so I wade across the first part

of the beach; paddle the last. I wish I was a better swimmer, a better anything. It's almost dark and I can't see any crabs or starfish or sea anemones. All the things that make me happy. A sob rises and chokes me. Why can't it be last summer in Mevagissey, when everything was fine?

I clamber up onto wet rocks, soaked clothes dragging. Shivering cold now. Then down into the next cove where there's a crescent of beach curving round, moon silvering the white round stones.

I see him sitting on a sand dune ledge, half hidden, like Cormoran trapped at the bottom of the pit. His clothes lie in a grumpy pile next to him and he's only wearing his shorts. I wonder if he got his shirt wet; if he's trying to get dry.

He hears the crunch of my footsteps on the small shale and looks up. Rubs his eyes as if he's been crying, though I can't really make out his face in the dark.

'I lost you, Dad,' I pant, limp with relief and not even mad at him, because I'm so glad I've found him again. 'What are you doing?'

'I don't know,' he says slowly, as if he's been asleep and I've just woken him.

I sit down next to him, grass prickling through the bottom of my soggy shorts. My feet and hands are gritty-damp with sand and everything's stinging from salt, but my hand finds his and for a moment I feel happy enough to laugh.

'I'm sorry,' he says, so quietly I barely hear him. 'I just kept walking, and I wasn't thinking and then I was here and I… and I…' He gasps and it's like he's holding his breath to dive. He's not even wet. I wonder how he dried off so quickly, or if he even went swimming at all. Or maybe he was waiting for me, and we were going to walk into the sea holding hands like we did last summer.

He lets out a big breath and a strangled laugh comes out. His hand flies away from mine to cover his face and I wonder if his heart feels like stone because of Mum leaving.

I think about the giant trapped down the well, and the little boy who got lost because he liked to walk in green places, and the trickle of blood on my knee last summer feathered by seawater; how Dad carried me all the way back.

Tears sequin his cheeks in between the vees of his fingers.

'I think you'll feel better after this,' I say, leaning my cheek on his arm.

LOSTWITHIEL

Shelley Trower

JO GREW UP here in the town of Lostwithiel. Whenever we visit her parents, our two children repeat what they've heard. Lost within the hills, they say, is where we're going.

A small town in the hills, either side of a tidal river. The river is sometimes just a few metres across, sometimes much wider. It has a bridge that is more than 700 years old. At low tide, the river flows through four of the six arches. At high tide, it flows through five. Two or three times a year, or when it floods, the river flows through all six arches. Last year, it flowed right over the bridge and into the riverside houses.

We come here from London in the holidays and spend a few nights with Jo's parents, and in summer months the children play in the river, as they do this hot afternoon. It's mid-tide, the river flowing through four and a half arches. The rough sandy-stone bottom of the fifth arch is only half submerged, and our children walk along the dry part under the bridge.

I can't see them now but they're old enough, seven and ten, to play together on their own for a minute. Bella and Ben, their brown curls always tangled. I exhale and lay back on the grassy bank, eyes closed, sun warm on my face. Water laps softly at the rivershore, birds and children do their chattering, small stones dig into my back.

It was just a few seconds I think, as I sit up, that I'd dozed, realising that I must have been dreaming the leeches sucking blood out my legs. I brush my hands over my legs at nothing there. And realise a silence, only the soft sound of the water this still day. I stand up and jump down the bank, following the way the children went a moment or so ago. There's only a thin strip of sand now and my feet get wet as I bend my way through the fifth arch. But I see no children on this other side of the bridge either, just the river, with its little mud-stone beaches. I shout their names, and the sound seems to ripple the water. I look back through the arch at the grassy bank, at nobody there either. I walk a little further upriver and shout again. I call Jo's phone in what I now suspect is still a dream, hearing my voice say things like I can't find the children, they went under the bridge, and they're gone. I look up at the hills that rise from either side of the river and wonder if they're getting lost within them. I look ahead at the trees that gather thickly further upriver until they become forest. I look into the water and see no signs, no splashes or body parts, not even a ripple now – nothing but a duck with a fish in its beak, a fish too large for it to eat.

The tide is high now. The river runs fully through all five arches.

I climb up the bank and look into the river from there. Still nothing. The water is clear today; they'd be visible even if they were underwater. I start walking along the bank, toward the trees. Until now I have felt too calm, as though nothing is real. Now I feel a flutter of something between panic and sorrow, something between searching frantically screaming their names and sitting on the ground to sob. I keep it all at bay and continue walking, calling for them every ten seconds or so. I hear Jo's shouts now as she has found her way to the river, and I shout back at her. People start gathering round, and I run back to her. Russell is among them, a retired policeman who lives on the corner of Jo's parents' street. Small town busybody, I'm thinking, as he stands there with his hands in his blue jeans pockets. And sure enough, here's old farmer Jago walking over, has to be in on everything, and suddenly I hate this parochial place. Luckily Jo is here to tell them calmly how we've lost our children – they've probably just got caught up in their game, she adds. Has anyone seen them: two messy brown-haired children wearing just shorts? A woman with her dog offers to walk up the back streets to look for them, and Russell and Jago offer to walk further downriver, taking any opportunity for a gossip. We decide to call the police in five minutes if there's no sign.

Jo and I continue again upriver, where we sense they'd have wanted to go, where there's the woods and a little clearing to the left up ahead, where a massive old tree is fallen, its roots exposed. They climbed all over that tree last summer, grazing their knees on its growling bark. They're not climbing on it now. There's just the ivy growing over it, a single bee crawling, looking tired. We stand there for a moment, watching the bee.

A slight breeze sends a chill through me, setting me off again towards the thicker trees, the beginning of the forest, Jo following close behind. As I enter the shadows a hint of smoke catches in my nose. D'you smell that, Jo asks, and we're pushing through the undergrowth, the smell growing into our lungs as brambles scratch our legs and arms – even Jo's cheek has gained a neat red line when I glance back at her, with a smudge of blood across her nose. We press on, stamping down the brambles, hacking against them with branch-sticks before we see another clearing in the shade, an area of sunlight. We barge on toward the light, until we burst out into it.

They are here, our two children, sat next to a small fire, eating fish. They don't see us straight away. The noise of the fire and their eating of fish keep their attention away from our entrance on the other side of the clearing. We stand there for a second, staring. We look around and it's just them, alone, with a side of trout each on a white dinner plate, picking at it awkwardly with a fork and putting flakes into their mouths. On the fire is a wire mesh on which the trout must have cooked. On the floor is a silver spatula that must have been used to lift the trout off onto the dinner plates. Astonished and suddenly furious, I shout at them what on earth are they doing, why did they leave the river, why didn't they tell me where they were going?

A woman wearing a deep brown hijab appears, and it is then I see a tent edging half in and out the trees. She's staying in the tent, I guess, or living in it. She looks at us, says hello. What's she doing here? We've got to get the children back to the river, I tell her, everyone is looking for them. Come on, I say to Jo, grabbing one of each child's hands and pulling them away, back into the trees, looking back and saying thank you, I guess, for the fish.

As we approach the river again, we see Russell and Jago and the dog-walking woman are gathered back together, cheering as they see the children with us. They got lost in the woods, we explain. Now they are found. The river is still high, flowing through the five arches.

Mum, our youngest starts, looking up at me as we walk back up the hill to Jo's parents' house, still in a daze. Mama, she says, looking at Jo: I didn't want the fish to start with, but actually it was tasty. Jo asks her again what happened, and this time Bella tells us they'd just gone a little way into the trees by themselves where they were playing with the piskies, and then they were lost. The way they thought went back to the river was just more and more trees. Then Amani had come and showed them the way to where the sweet berries grow. She'd taken their hands, and the children followed her because they didn't know what other way to go. And Amani led them in further, until she sat them down next to the fire and put the fish on the fire and one minute later gave them the fish.

You should never go off with strangers, you know that, Jo says to them. They tell us she isn't a stranger; we've seen her before. I don't believe them, but I'm glad they're found and we're coming to Jo's parents' house, so I leave it.

Later, Jo tells me she wants to take some food to Amani, see if she needs anything. I tell her she should stay away. But Jo goes anyway, taking apples, carrots, and hazelnuts. I run after her to catch up, leaving the children with Jo's parents, shouting back that we won't be long. Jo takes my hand and we walk down the hill together, over the bridge with the river fallen to four arches, and retrace the way through the trees. The shadows are longer now. As we get to the clearing, we hear voices and slow down. We peer through the trees and see more than Amani: there's about six adults in the shadows, and three children. Jo steps out, offering the food. I creep behind her. Amani sees us and smiles, starts thanking us and offering a place around the fire, and as we stand there hesitating about getting back to our children, we're amazed to see Russell walk in another way through the trees.

What are you doing here, Jo and Russell ask each other the same. Jo says we brought food; Russell says he's been coming from time to time, since the group arrived. He asks us to please never breathe a word. Not even to Jo's parents, because just one person will tell just one person until the wrong person knows. We promise, and he sits us down. He tells us slowly now, about how he's part of a network stretching to the coast, consisting of a bunch of nosy old busybodies who pretend to be a bunch of nosy old busybodies but who secretly assist people who come to shore. This group in the trees had come halfway upriver one night, on a small fishing boat on a high spring tide. Russell's friends had loaned them four canoes to help them travel further upriver. They paddled under the bridge of a crescent moon when the river flowed through all six arches. They're living here in the woods, for now.

Old farmer Jago is in on it too, he tells us as the sun sparkles low in the leaves. He shows us the two wooden huts they're building for the coming winter. But he's a right-wing anti-immigrant GB News watcher, I say, remembering the winter evening we'd seen it flickering through his open curtains. I wonder now if that's part of his disguise.

These people from afar, they give us fish by their fire and show us the real meaning of Lostwithiel. It doesn't mean lost within the hills, not at all. It derives from the old Cornish word Lostgwydeyel, so they heard. Lostgwydeyel means the place at the tail of the woodland. The woodland has a tail, because it is a living being. Up here in the woods is the heart.

TRICKED BY THE QUEEN OF FEY

Ella Walsworth-Bell

BEFORE GOING to the pub, I take a quick stroll, to pluck up courage. Turn along the lane out of the village, my smart shoes softly tap-tapping on the tarmac. A few early stars shine bright in the clear autumn sky and my stomach does somersaults. Internet dating? Me? I must be nuts. I nearly walk back to the farm then and there.

I stride the grassy track leading uphill, dew speckling the ends of my trousers. My daughter's words come to mind. Too old to pick and choose, she'd said. Try it. You're not going to meet anyone new, milking those ruddy cows every day.

I sigh, catching a whiff of my freshly ironed shirt, all mixed in with the smell of bracken in the hedgerows. She's right. I need a woman. Need a change. Need to get out the damn door once in a while. Five years since my wife Morwenna died. All I've done in the meantime is run the farm. Dawn until sundown, five years straight. Going out for a meal with someone would be good for me.

I stop dead, at the stone. This seemed enormous to me when I was a child. It towers ten foot high – a rounded oblong shape that seems out of kilter with the moorland landscape around it.

Blisland Stone. Tourists call it the Jubilee Rock. We villagers simply know it as the Stone.

I run my work roughened hands over the lichen-bearded granite. The rock is covered with carvings, like tattoos on a fairground freak. Some are relatively recent: coats of arms from rich families at the turn of the century.

The Stone is older than that, though. In fact, it's the most ancient piece of granite on Bodmin Moor. Some say it predates humankind.

I crouch at the back of the Stone, feeling down for the secret symbols half-hidden by long strands of grass. Here there are jagged lines, off-centre squares, oddly dotted circles. The information board they've put up says these could be runes, dating from Viking times.

I know better, or think I do.

They're ancient as the land itself, and they hold

power.

I trace one with my finger, squinting in the half-light. Everything is greyed out, shaded to black and white, now that the sun's rays have gone from the sky. I do what I always do, and run my hand backwards along the line, three times for luck. The lichen crackles into fragments under my fingers.

It's done, and I'm ready for this bloody date now. I stride back downhill, and the lights of the village draw me in like a moth to a bonfire.

A clear night.

And yet, as I walk downhill towards the houses, my skin prickles. A thick mist shrouds the pub. I blink. Sometimes we do get a convection fog up here, in the summer months. Everywhere else in Cornwall can be broad sunshine, and we get a strange white obscurity in the air of the high moors.

But I've never seen it on a crisp autumnal evening. I smell a strange floral scent, but there are few blooms in the hedgerow this time of year. I close my eyes for a second, trying to place it. When I open them again, my vision flickers. Just briefly, as if the world itself has adjusted.

It isn't mist. More like a visual thing. I blink, and feel in the pocket of my wax jacket to check for my glasses. I'm forty-two and like to think I don't need them. I'll be lucky if any woman'll want me.

I stand at the door of the Blisland Inn and my heart races. John Hick, out on a date with a stranger. I breathe in deep and push open the oak door.

She said in her email that she'd get there at seven o'clock sharp and go to the table by the window. Well, I'm never on time and I know it's a bad start to any relationship, but I walk straight across the pub floor to the bar. I can't do this without a pint of ale in my hand. My mouth waters. I don't look left or right, but I hear a low hubbub of voices and the crackle of flames from the fire. There's the smell of woodsmoke and the slate flagstones are smooth under my feet.

You'd think I'd want a date farther away from my own village, my own farm. Away from the prying eyes of neighbours.

But no – I'm honest, always have been. If I'm dating, I'd rather do it in the open space of my local pub. Let people talk if they must. I've been brought up with these men and women, and they're all familiar faces.

I don't recognise the barmaid as being a local, but that doesn't stop me ordering a pint of bitter and grasping the glass thankfully. My stomach churns with hunger after a day in the fields.

Hang on. That barmaid. She's gorgeous.

She stares at me with beguiling green eyes which dance with reflections from the fire behind me. She's unsmiling and yet her face is fine-featured. Her long fair hair is streaked with silver, and I fancy for a moment there are strands of gold along her skin, caught in the wrinkles around her eyes. She wears dangly earrings: on one side is a tiny silver sun, on the other is a wide full moon. I smile, starstruck, and pass her a five-pound note. As she spins around to work the till, I breathe out and my heart stumbles to a steady pace. I'd been holding my breath, but don't know why. This barmaid, she's not my type, and I'm not here for her anyway.

Turning, I scan the room for someone sitting on their own.

A dark-haired woman catches my eye, and waves. I nod and walk over.

'You must be John,' she says, and I go to take a seat opposite her.

'Eve, isn't it?' I put down my pint, and it slops onto the varnished wood of the table. My hands are chattering with nerves, and I pull them back onto my knees, stretching out my fingers to ease the tension.

'You nervous?' she asks, and her voice is the same relaxed tone as when she called me on the phone, the other night. Perhaps she thought I was going to stand her up, and she wanted to check the number worked.

'A bit.' I nod, slowly. 'It's not my thing, this internet dating lark.'

'And I'm your first, aren't I?' She smiles, and it's

genuine. She's trying to put me at ease. 'It's nice to be someone's first. Haven't been one of those in a long time.'

I chuckle, 'Done this before then, have you?'

'Not for a while.' A shadow shifts across her face. 'I – I lost someone dear to me. In fact, I've lost a few.'

'My wife passed away five years to the day. Daughter signed me up to the website, said it'd do me good.' I smile apologetically and reach for my drink, then pause. 'Dunno if I'm ready, but here I am.'

She nods, and tips her head sideways, listening. Her hair's curly and it bounces on her shoulders. 'You're looking good though, John. I mean, smartly dressed and that.'

I shift in my seat. 'Clean shirt is all. Should've seen me when I come off the fields earlier. Live in my overalls most days. Covered in, well, you know. I'm a dairy farmer. Got a herd of a hundred, give or take. Keeps me busy enough.'

'If you've been out all day, you'll need feeding.' She hands me a menu and I reach for it. My hand's shaking, and she laughs. 'Look at that! Shivery with hunger, you are.'

'Let's see what we fancy.' I open the menu in front of me but the words swim in front of my eyes. I daren't sip my pint; I'm feeling anxious enough as it is.

Instead, I look at her closely. It was the eyes and the hair that I liked on her photo, and I still do. Reminded me of someone, from years back. Different from my wife's red curls and freckled skin, and God knows I need different.

I landed on this Eve, and I'm not so sure she was telling the truth about herself. Is she like her picture, or no?

I took my photo the day I posted it. Standing in the fields, feeling like a loon, with green fields and blue skies. Looking like the farmer I am. There's wrinkles on my forehead from the hard winters, and my neck's thick as a bullock. I wouldn't win any races, but my forearms are muscled from driving tractors across icy rutted fields.

I thought her photo was an old one, taken when she was younger. I frown, trying to make out what's clanging in my head like a warning bell. Something's off. I've a gut feeling – like at the auction, when I'm being done over for an animal that's advertised the wrong age.

'Quick question, Eve.'

She looks up, eyes all innocent. As she holds the menu, I notice her silver Celtic rings, intricate and beautiful. Suddenly, I can visualise her in bed with me quick as a flash. She'd writhe around, her hair loose on my pillow. I'd hold her tight against my chest, and she'd smell great.

'It's silly, really. I just wondered...'

'I'm not after your money, if that's what you're thinking.'

I laugh. 'No, it's just... you're... looking really good for your age. You're the same age as me, you know?'

'And how do you know that so exactly, Mr. Hick of a hundred cows?'

My laughter tails off. 'Well...your age was on the site, see. And I'm forty-two as well.'

She frowns, as if trying to work something out. 'Really?'

'Yup. And... you look bloody amazing for forty-two.'

She frowns again, then chuckles. 'Honestly. If I was going to lie about my age, I'd have gone the other way, you daft bugger. Pretended to be twenty-one or something.' She puts the menu down. 'What's good here?' she asks.

'Haven't been here in years, to be honest. But food's always good.' I close my menu, running my hands over the black smooth cover. 'I've chosen.'

'And?'

'Steak and ale pie.' I nod toward the bar, gesturing for the barmaid to come and take our order.

'Oh, don't rush me.' She sips wine. 'I'm making the most of this. My night out. What about the pheasant in red wine?'

'I've a herd of cattle, remember? Always recommend the beef, in any form.'

'That's it, then.' She flashes me a contrary look, and I warm to her. 'I'm going for the pheasant, John. I like the wildness of it.'

'Not wild enough though, are they? Farmed down in the valleys, penned and fed up… then let loose to be shot by the posho's one weekend a year.'

'Can't put me off.' She unwraps her knife and fork, and they shine against the varnished wood of the table.

The barmaid's come for our order and I glance at her. She watches me with her icy green eyes, and I can't look away. Something's certainly in the air tonight, something special. My blood's rising. I'm getting so as I want to hold someone tight, and yet I've got to play this dating game all evening.

I lean against the hard oak back of my chair. 'Steak and ale pie for me, and the pheasant for this young lady.'

'Less of the young, please. I sound like your daughter or something.'

The barmaid scratches her pen on the pad. 'And to drink?'

'We're fine, I think,' Eve says, 'Oh, hang on, though.' She tips up her glass, and the red vanishes to the back of her throat. 'One more, please. And a jug of water, if I may.' She smiles, waiting for her to leave.

I'm not sure what to talk about, and I fidget. The fire is suddenly too warm, and the room spins. 'I don't feel great,' I say.

'You do look a touch pale.'

I reach for the window next to me, and try to manoeuvre the catch to let some air in. It's jammed. Damn thing. I give up and meet her eye.

She talks, as the barmaid brings her wine. 'So, tell me about yourself. Not that garbage on your profile. What life really means to you.'

I lean my elbows on the table. 'Well, I was brought up here. In the village. Lived on the farm all my life, inherited it young.'

'Did you never want to leave? To travel?'

I shrug. 'Nah. Well, maybe…when I was a teenager.' I stop, not wanting to remember. 'Before then, though, when I was a kid – living here was heaven. All that moorland, the rivers to muck about in. I love it. Not just the fields and the farm, but the Moor itself. It's part of me.' I break off, embarrassed.

'It is gorgeous up here, you're right.'

'And whereabouts are you from?'

She smiles. 'Funny you should ask. I lived in this village, for a bit, when I was young.'

'Really?' I shuffle my cutlery to one side. I lean closer, staring. 'When? I mean, if you're the same age as me…'

'Would have been about seven or so.'

I stare at her. Trying to figure it out. Trying to place her. The school's tiny, and back then it was even tinier.

'Evelyn? From Miss Taylor's class?'

I look at her dark curls, smell woodsmoke from the fire, and grip the edge of the table with hands that are white at the knuckle.

I blink, and in my head we're out there, up on the moors, after school. I'm a boy in short trousers and my hands are black with peat-mud. Evelyn had persuaded me to dam the stream, and she stood in the middle of the water, her red gingham school dress tucked into her knickers, a devil-may-care attitude on her face. I finished and smiled at her, triumphant. The water pooled at her feet and deepened, puddling and trickling at the edges.

'That's done it.' I smacked pebbles into the gaps, shoved in handfuls of gritty mud. 'Water won't break through this.'

She laughed, and the water bulged and trickled over the dam. 'It's going anyway, Johnnie. Let's smash it.'

We'd kicked down the damn then whooped with laughter as the water rushed away downstream, running clear. A skylark called, singing her high-pitched tune. We'd paid no mind.

'What're we doing next, Evelyn?' I had to ask,

every time. And every time it was the same answer.

'Gonna go find the faeries.' She'd leapt out of the water and ran barefoot up the hillside, skipping ahead, her dark hair dancing in the wind. I grabbed her sandals and scrambled after her.

We made it to the top of Rough Tor, and I handed her sandals back. We searched among the stones and bushes.

'It won't be much,' she said, 'Just a little sign. A clump of grass tied in a knot. Stones in a ring. Something like that.'

'Like this?' I squinted at a tumbled cluster of sheep droppings, tried to pretend I knew what she meant.

'Oh, Johnny. You are funny. That's poo. Not faery-stuff. You're not looking hard enough.'

At tea-time, my stomach had grumbled, and I'd persuaded her homeward.

I look at the woman opposite me, trying to fit her face to that girl with flyaway hair and a vivid imagination. I frown. Evelyn had moved out of the village mid-way through primary school and my heart had ached with sadness. The other boys were into football; the girls into Barbie princesses. No-one wanted to search on the high moors for faery rings like my friend Evelyn.

She smiles at me, leans forward across the table and I smell her perfume, sharp and sweet. 'Do you remember me, Johnny?'

'You knew! You knew and made me guess!'

'All part of the game, Johnny. All part of the game.'

She has the same eyes. The same hair, if I look closely.

'I didn't recognise you, Evelyn. Or are you Eve now?'

'Well...'

'So? What happened, where did you end up?'

'Oh, we travelled all over, when I was a kid. Then... I had a partner, and a little boy. Went back to college when we split up. Studied history at Exeter, then a masters in mythology.'

I shake my head. She's bound to be out of my league. I was never one for the books, myself. 'You always were too clever for me. All I am is a farmer. Always was going to be.'

'Nothing wrong with that. You're grounded. Safe, I mean. You knew where you were going to stay, and you're right here.'

Her eyes flick to the door behind me and it closes after someone. She tightens her lips and there's a flicker of recognition in her eyes. I turn my head. A young man in jeans and tee-shirt has walked into the pub. He's rubbing his eyes as if he's been out at a rock concert, and he's only just woken up.

Her voice lowers. 'Look Johnny, it's complicated, this. My son... I haven't seen him for a long time. I miss him, you know?'

She startles at the sound of a footstep next to the table. It's the barmaid with our meals, and the food steams on the plates. I unwrap my knife and fork, slowly.

'Any ketchup, or sauces at all?' The woman hesitates.

I shake my head. I want to talk to Eve, learn more about her. Where she'd lived, what she'd been up to, exactly what she'd been studying. My mouth salivates and I breathe in the steam of my steak and ale pie.

Eve's eyes flash at me as I stab into the golden crust. 'Don't! For God's sake, don't eat it!'

The barmaid waits, smiling. Her elfin face looks down at us and I fancy her cruel suddenly. She waits, like a hungry raven watching baby birds in a nest.

'Eve. You okay? It's just steak and ale pie.'

'Don't touch it. Please. It's a trick.'

I look up. The fire flickers bright green in the grate. Burns down, then flares high, as if snatched by a gust of wind. The people in the room are statue-still, stuck at their tables with cutlery poised in the air like weapons. I gasp for breath, and smell spring wildflowers. Am I having a stroke? Is this it – the end? Too much excitement for a middle-aged man?

'Eve. Evelyn?'

She stares over my shoulder, then straight at the

barmaid, as if she knows her, too. She's cross, or upset, or both. 'You tricked me. You said you wouldn't. You promised.'

The woman smiles gracefully like an apologetic politician. She speaks, and my ears tingle. Now, her voice is silver bells, whistles and flutes, sharp and fine as linnet-song. I clamp my hands over my ears, but I still hear her, as if she's speaking in my head.

'I never play fair, mortal ones. You should know that, you of all people. And this is so much more fun. Now, look who's here to join us for dinner.'

Eve waves, frantically, at the person behind me.

'Mum?' The young man's voice echoes, concerned. 'Mum? You alright?'

She stands, knocking her glass over. Red wine splotches her flowered dress.

'Get out, James,' she says, then switches to a low persuasive tone, 'It's only a dream, love. Don't stay here. Just go right out that door and you'll wake up. It'll all be fine in the morning.'

'Mum?' he says again, but it's confused this time, and the door slams shut after he leaves.

Eve stays upright, face-to-face with the strange woman. 'You've had your game – I've seen my son. Now let this one go. Please, your majesty.'

'Oh, my Evelyn. You know the rules, better than I.' She shakes her head, and there's that scent of flowers again. Night-scented stock, it is. I recognise it from the kitchen garden, back home.

The woman laughs, and viridescent fire dances around the logs in the grate, and I think I hear pixie-song.

My date stands up for me. 'He hasn't. I swear he hasn't touched it.'

I look down at my pie. The fork drops from my fingertips.

'Evelyn?' I ask. 'Where exactly are we? And what happens if I eat this?'

She leans forward, sweeping my meal onto the flagstones of the floor. The plate smashes into shards of white china on the dark slate and the pie-dish sings out a high note. The other diners stay stock-still. If this is a dream – and perhaps it is – then I'm stuck inside of it. With my old friend Evelyn, who I haven't seen for thirty-five years.

Evelyn looks down, embarrassed. 'Well, Johnnie, it's like this. I had a research project I was working on. Finding evidence. Of ancient myths. And... faeries. It went wrong. I went too far.'

Fear shoots a bolt into my heart. 'Who are you?' I ask the green-eyed woman, and I know the answer already.

She laughs, and her eyes are cruel. 'I'm the Queen of Fey. You're mine, like the other one there. Mine until the end of time. If any sustenance reaches your lips, I've won you.'

'But he didn't...' Evelyn's eyes stop at my pint, sitting on the table in front of me. It's four-fifths full.

'Oh yes. Oh yes, he did.' She points, and my stomach twists a fresh somersault. I glance sideways at the table, like a naughty schoolboy.

'Hang on, ma'am.' I push back the chair, and its oak legs scrape against the stones. The sound pulls me back, and my head clears as if I've taken a breath of fresh moorland air. 'Just you hang on.'

I stand taller than her and I hold myself strong, staring her down.

'I'm a farmer from Blisland and I called for protection from the Stone before I came here. You've got nothing on me. Look at the table.'

Both women stare down at the varnished wood.

There's a mucky puddle of slopped beer around my glass.

'I spilt it. Not like me to chuck good ale around, but I was nervous.'

Evelyn's eyes widen.

I seize the moment and reach for her hand. It's soft, and warm, and for a moment I'm back in my childhood.

The barmaid, or queen, or whoever she thinks she is, narrows her eyes.

I haul Evelyn towards me. 'We're leaving.'

She reaches out for Evelyn and her voice turns to

rock. 'She's mine.'

'Not anymore,' I say, and dash for the door, holding my date's hand fast.

I push open the oak door and a burst of fresh air hits my face. My legs feel stronger, now I'm away from that infernal warmth and that strange fire. I breathe in deep and look at Evelyn. Her face is excited and fearful, all at once. There's a howl of rage from inside the pub, and the sound of a solid table crashing onto the floor.

'Time to head home to the farm. The Stone's on the way.'

Tears brim in her eyes. 'Am I safe? Am I?'

I look around me at the clear autumn air, and the sprinkling of stars, all in the same places as earlier. A blackbird flits across the green and the sounds fade to the simplicity of a calm night.

'Yes. We're back. And she can't interfere if I've touched the Stone. I always do. No-one can take a Blisland man.'

She smiles, and leans on my shoulder, puffing out a breath of air. 'I hoped you hadn't changed. And you haven't, Johnnie. Let's go home.'

THE LOOKING GLASS

Karen Taylor

*'TAKE A good look at yourself. Look what you've become.'
At the time I thought my mother's words harsh, a spiteful
outburst for no good reason. She'd steered me to the mirror in
her small low-ceilinged bungalow, the early spring light beaming
on glass, showing me exactly what she meant. It was an ugly
sight.*

*'You're a divorcee, not a zombie. You need a holiday,' she'd
added for good measure.*

And so, I took one.

The looking glass definitely tricked me into picking it
up. The last thing I expected to see while strolling on
a Cornish beach was a mirror. A pool of light slap-
bang in the middle of the shingles. An alien landing
pad bright and shiny. I snuck over to the object with

the wariness of a crab. When I looked down it clouded over; my own face, framed in black ringlets of seaweed, peered back. It was a strange sight. My face, freckled with sand, a beached sea urchin.

We looked at each other for a short while. Me and my sandy alter-ego. I rubbed my eyes and yawned. Freckle-face winked. What! I widened my eyes; my mouth fell open in shock. My reflection smiled back at me. I touched my pulse. It was racing. I wasn't dead.

This 'other' me, smug in the shingles, gave me another cheeky wink. When was the last time I had looked cheeky … or winked, for that matter? A trick of the light? I looked up at the sky and the sun was still shining. The earth, as far as I was aware, was still turning. Freckles was looking amused when I glanced back down. She raised an eyebrow.

'So, are you ready for our See Voyage?' she said in a voice which sounded like mine, but better; like it had been caressed by a warm sea breeze.

I looked around. A man was walking a dog by the edge of the water. Way out on the ocean was a liner. On the beach below was an oval of glass and a reflection of me waiting for an answer.

'So how is this going to work?' I replied. I was used to arguing the toss with myself. In an insane world talking to my better half in the reflection of a mirror on a pebbly beach didn't seem unreasonable.

'Like I said. We're going on a See Voyage. We're going to take that little red boat bobbing away in the shallows.'

'What little red boat bobbing away in the shallows?' I turned around. No little red boat, just a man and a dog walking west towards the lighthouse.

'The red boat in the mirror. Behind me. Be careful when you pick me up... I'm fragile.'

I felt oddly reassured. This cocky 'mirror me' wasn't all show. When I held it in my hand, I noticed a fine crack running down the right-hand side of the glass. Glass framed in mother of pearl, a pink and gauzy grey. I held it to my face, looked my reflection in the eye. Using my sleeve, I wiped away a covering of specks of sand and debris. Close up it looked older, the glass cloudy and mottled. Seaweed hair extensions stuck stubbornly to its slender frame. So, I left them there to swish in the breeze. There was something endearing about this little touch of vanity.

'Shall we embark?' My reflection said through pursed lips. 'To the boat,' she continued. 'The one …'

'I know, just behind you.'

'Finishing my sentences now,' Mirrorme said, with a superior smirk.

'We have so much in common.'

'And yet so little,' smarty-pants replied. I wondered if she could read my mind, as well as my face.

'Hold me out in front of you and I will lead the way,' she commanded.

This was easier said than done. The mirror's perspective was deceptive, like the rear-view camera screens in cars. I tripped on the extended lead of a Highland terrier, I stubbed my foot on a rock, banged my shin on the side of the little red boat. It bobbed back in the water apologetically.

'Everything looks so distant in the mirror. Not right in your face like in real life.'

'Lesson One for the day,' Mirrorme said.

'You mean there are more lessons to be learnt before I wake up?'

'Lesson Two. Reality is in the eye of the beholder. Let's do history next.'

Perhaps I should have been afraid, with the sea lapping around my ankles, an ocean stretching to infinity. But I wasn't. For the first time in a very long time the anticipation of doing something mad and potentially dangerous was exciting. I just wished I knew how to sail.

The boat was bobbing up and down expectantly. Mirrorme was fixing me with her glassy eye when I turned back to her.

'You've done this before, remember? Shall I jog your memory?' The mirror misted over for a second before revealing an old movie of myself on a small dart yacht. Must have been 20 years ago. We were holidaying in Sardinia, one of those all-inclusive family-friendly holiday clubs, and I'd done a sailing course. I was good at it, I recalled. Sailing was all about tacking and balance. Working with the tides and the prevailing wind.

Placing the mirror on the wooden slat of a seat, I pushed the boat out to sea and hopped on board. There was just enough wind to get some movement. The worst thing about any water sport, I remembered, was the static lulls. Today we had a balmy breeze; Mirrorme's ringlets were fluttering like the sails. I propped her up against my rucksack and we sailed the waves in tandem. From the corner of my eye, I could see the sky reflected in the glass; the gulls swooping, a line of little clouds puffing above the ocean like steam from a train.

I moved from side to side on the boat, pulling at the sail ropes, steering our course over the waves. I had no idea where we were going.

'Well, this is nice,' I said after a while. A long while. And it really had been nice, with the sun and sea breeze on my face, sailing with a sense of purpose, but with no real destination.

When I looked back at Mirrorme I was surprised to see a trail of water running down the glass. Was she crying? Foolish thought. It was raining. First small splashes and then torrents. The weather in Cornwall can be bipolar and the wind was whipping up the waves, making the boat rock violently. I grabbed the mirror as it jolted off its perch. Mirrorme was looking ahead towards the promenade in Penzance. Waves lashed the sea wall, froth gushing like geysers. In the mirror I could see grey shapes circling the boat. Fins. For Chrissake. Fins! Unlike me, Mirrorme was wearing a noble, brave expression. It could have been carved out of wood, a figurehead for the bow of an old ship.

'Lesson Three,' Mirrorme said.

'What!' I screamed over the howling wind.

'Always look for a safe harbour in a storm.'

'I learnt to tack in the Mediterranean not the Celtic Sea!' I could see a light blinking to the east. The lighthouse? The light was pulsing in time with the high waves crashing against its stone turret, drenching it with foam. It didn't look like a safe harbour, and I couldn't steer the boat to it, regardless. In one hand I clutched the looking glass, in the other the sail ropes. I was clutching on to soggy strands of hope. And then I had a lighthouse moment. The mirror. There were still some faint rays of light piercing through the clouds. The clouds had grown, formed an aggressive gang, but light was still squeezing through. I held up the mirror, turning it in my hand, trying to recreate the SOS signal, spitting out water as the sea flung itself at me.

It all seemed pointless. I was going to die a horrible watery death because I had dared to dream. Dared to do one more reckless thing. The mirror and my raised arm were getting battered by the wind and rain. I let my arm fall to my side.

'It's raining men. Hallelujah. It's raining men. Amen,' Mirrome was singing. Her grainy little voice was singing. It was all right for her. She would float down to the bottom of the ocean to be picked up by adorable mermaids or be washed up in Hawaii … maybe. Me… I was shark snack. I was the bloated corpse found by wild swimmers in Sennen Cove.

I looked in the mirror. 'What have you got to smile about?'

'It's raining men. Hallelujah,' she sang back, as a school of dolphins leapt out of the ocean, pirouetting like backing dancers. 'And you're gonna get absolutely soaking wet.'

'Tell me something I don't know,' I replied, cut off by a mouthful of sea water.

The dolphins were surrounding the boat. I'd read somewhere about how they steer people to safety. Had actually nudged a child to the shore. Just being by our side gave us some protection from the waves. I pulled at the ropes, steering us towards land.

'Ahoy there. Ahoy there.' Mirrorme was spouting off again. I was sitting on the mirror as both my hands were busy with the ropes.

'Thanks,' she said, as I budged over and lifted her up.

Her eyes were looking towards the harbour. I took the hint and started to flash the mirror again. In the distance I could see boats in the harbour, all safely moored but still taking a beating from the storm. To the west there was something moving on the sea. At first it looked like it might be an orange buoy which had been cast loose. But it was approaching fast, smashing over the waves. It was a RIB lifeboat.

'Thank God. Thank God! I cried, hugging the mirror to me with one hand, still clutching the ropes with the other.

'Thank yourself.'

'And the dolphins,' I replied.

'Goes without saying.'

An hour later I was sitting in The Dolphin pub in Penzance Harbour drinking cider. I'd already had a tot of rum on the lifeboat over. I'd brushed off all attempts to rush me to A&E and, once released from my foil wrapping, I was warming myself by a log-burning fire, wearing oversized fishermen's joggers and a 'I Heart Cornwall' sweatshirt.

My rucksack had survived. So had the mirror which was stowed inside. The little red boat, which had slipped its mooring and floated to the beach, had been returned to the harbour. No questions asked. Thankfully.

'It's raining men.' I couldn't get the damn song out of my mind. But I couldn't help noticing, The Dolphin was full of them. A pub on the corner of the harbour... hardly surprising that the local sailors and fishermen hung out there. My two rescuers were sitting at the table with me, laughing about my 'trip', the 'foolhardiness of tourists'. 'Hadn't I checked the weather forecast?' 'Did I really think it was advisable to jump into a random boat and head off, on my own, out to sea?'

The guy probing me had the look of Paul Hollywood questioning a baker about their dubious plans for a *Bake Off* showstopper. He had the same flirty eyes. I figured he must have a tourist in every port. I was itching to get in my bag and check my look in the mirror. I'd used the looking glass earlier to fix my face before going into the pub. I was pleased to see the reflection looking back at me was reassuringly healthy. Cheeky, even. It winked back … but only at the same time as I winked. I tried a few quick moves, just to check this was my actual reflection. It was. Sadly, it was.

The stars were out as I strolled back to my hotel. We must have sat in the pub for two hours or more, the handsome sailor and me. Turns out he is also divorced, and a local carpenter who volunteers for the RNLI. A Cornishman. We're meeting tomorrow evening for dinner. I'll return his clothes then. But, tonight, I'll return another gift.

The gang of clouds which had bullied me on the boat were nowhere in sight. Instead, a full moon blazed in the night sky, illuminating the calm sea so it shone like sheet glass. I walked down the rugged rock steps onto the beach, where I'd picked up the looking glass that afternoon. There were a few people out walking, even at that late hour.

I sat there for some time, just watching the waves rolling in and rolling out. The looking glass was propped up against my rucksack and every now and then I glanced over to check if Mirrorme was there. But no. The only things reflected in the glass were the moon and stars and sea birds flying home to roost.

It must have been midnight when I rose to leave. I placed the glass on the sand, circling it with seashells and draping the frame with strands of seaweed. I took one last look in the mirror. A good look. It was a beautiful sight.

PEDN VOUNDER

Rebecca Johnson Bista

'THEY SAYS I've lost my nerve,' Mal told me that evening when I met him coming up the path from Treen. '*Gone soft he has*, I heard your old man tellin' Jess Jewill, the one they're callin' gaffer now.'

'Wouldn't think to say a bad word about your Da but sneerin', he were. And him as I thought were my partner in anythin' after that time two year ago, you remember? When we brought them boats in after the big October storm.' Mal paused, then added, 'But how could you forget?'

Weren't a cold day. Wind had dropped briefly, but Mal was shrugged up in his jacket set for heading into a squall when I stopped to greet him. He didn't look over keen to see me, though I was never sorry for the times we met. But he talked, and once he'd begun, I could see there was something in him winched up that tight he could scarcely hold it.

'Soft, am I?' He pushed his big face forward, almost into mine. I didn't flinch. 'Well, an' maybe they're right,' he added, withdrawing again, dropping his voice like he'd had second thoughts about me.

So I asked Mal how come he'd heard them say that, was he sure? Knowing it weren't like my Da to call no man a coward that'd ride a trawler in the big swells, nor one that ever had.

'Was comin' down-along the harbour front at Newlyn this mornin' after checkin' the gear on the boats. That's when I came across 'em. Your father haulin' the hawsers up off the trawl beam onto the walkway, talkin' all the while to Jess stackin' the creels beside him.

'Reckon they didn't hear me comin'. The wind took their words like scraps of bait chewed off a line an' spat 'em out at me in gobbets. *Weren't none of his what got injured, that night, were it?* they says.'

Mal turned and looked out to the headland where the big slabs of granite are shuffled up right on the edge of balance, then on out over the swollen Atlantic, dull as a pewter pot in the fading light. It was like he found it hard to keep his gaze on me while he was talking.

I tried to stop him. I started to say it couldn't be

like that, it was Mal pulled me out of the water. Da know'd it weren't about having no bottle; must be some other feller, or something else. No-one'd hold it against him for what happened, or for not going back in the sea.

Don't know if he heard me proper, with the wind against me. He was well ahead on the path when he looked back, standing above the cliff where the steps go down to the beach. Mal cut them steps himself, must be ten, twelve year back when I was a child.

'I still knows my way down Pedn back'ards an' in the dark,' he called out. 'Even in the mud an' the weather.'

The wind brought his words to me as if he was still by my side. His eyes were narrowed in the breeze, his face set broad. I thought he was smiling, then, before he walked off where I couldn't follow.

I know my way down that cliff, too – the way Mal climbed down the vounder that evening to the beach. Know every footstep between the sharp boulders and the hebe scrub, on that path so narrow at places that one trip on a root could send you pitching over the cliff edge to the rocks below. And I know how at night, after a fair day, you can feel the heat of the earth coming up like the cliff's a living body breathing quietly under you in the dark.

We used to go down there before dawn at low tide

to look for jetsam – anything really – that might have got stranded on the shore between the headlands, or in the lagoon between the sandbar and the beach.

Don't know what Mal was heading down there for that evening, though. Maybe nothing in particular. Maybe same as we used to. Or maybe because it's a good place to walk off your trouble if you can. Wind whips it out of you with salty slaps if you set your face to the ocean. Even just to see the sea glitter under the smallest sliver of moon – the way it burnishes the water in a streak like a polished blade – will turn your spirits. That's how I try to remember it.

I like to think that'd be how it was for Mal, too. On the way down the cliff, he'd have stopped to look out over the bay to the taut curve of the horizon: a thin, bright line where the sun left its dying trail. He'd have picked his way down through the furze and the glossy leaves of the hebe, with the green and cobalt colours bleaching out to greys in the half-light. And the sound of the sea would have washed out his sour spirits, filling him with its energy.

And I can't help thinking about what must've happened next, even though I don't want to. Don't know when he'd have seen the dark shape in the water, cliff's too high to see it from the top, that's for sure. Maybe twenty yards from the sand, and him knowing it'd be too late to go back for help by then.

He'd have gone the last scramble down the rocks, feet slipping out of the footholds in his speed, in the spray and the oncoming dark, and jumped down onto the small patch of sand.

Tide was rising so it would've been coming up the beach fast, swallowing the sandbar in the bay, out where the boat was. Currents are wicked right then, spinning off the edges of the bar in all directions; boat could have been pulled out anyways, or sent smashing into the rocks. But still shallow enough for a grown man to wade out there, if you were wise to stay clear of the fast water.

And Mal would've known every minute counted. He knew the currents and the risk – must've known – and still he waded out there. Found the boy and the girl bundled up together, both nigh on drownded and washed up on the spit of sand, waves tugging at their legs like they was only a bit o' weed. I can just hear the way the lad might have been saying, hoarse-like from the water: 'Take the child, take her first, Mister, go on.'

Can't think too much about what must've gone through Mal's mind that minute he walked into the sea, and him not set foot in water this two-and-a-half year gone. Da said that time, back then, he saw Mal tip up his head as he went through the waves and his mouth was wide open like he was roaring at the sea. But no sound came out that Da could hear, and if there was any it was slammed back down Mal's throat, stifled by the wind on the water.

So I can just hear the boy calling out to him as he hesitated, 'Mister, what you doin'? Take hold of the child and I can help myself then.' And the girl close to finished, cold and clammy in his hands. Their boat was smashed up on the rocks, splintered at the bow when it hit the cliff where land spits out stone into the water, roughing it up into foam. Little skiff it were, blue-painted. Kids like that, they should never have been out in such weather.

Mal would've shipped the girl over his shoulder, just a bundle of clothes in his big hands. Taken her up to the rocks out of the surge, leaving the boy marooned on the sandbar as the tide came in. Waves would've been cutting off the path back up the rocks, then sucking out again in a deep gurgle, churning the tiny shells and stones that shred your skin like a grater when the sea drags the sand over you. And the currents were crashing the waves across the cove, so they boiled round the base of the rock.

He came back in the water for a second time, did Mal, his fists clenched, his eyes like a ranting preacher all hellfire and damnation, near sparks flying from him, cutting his big body through the waves. He got to the boy, and he took him by the collar and began to drag and drag, all the time staring into his eyes like a savage beast, dragging him through the plunging water – just like he did with me. Losing his footing, going under in the boil and surge of the breakers, and coming up again spitting like a whale.

They were both near done for, as I see it, dragging each other. Each of them trying to get a handhold on a steady bit o' rock to pull on where the waves would boost them upward and out. And Mal got his hand in a crevice and began to haul himself up, still grasping the boy's jacket, and pulling him after. The boy had his body against the rock, waves washing over his head by now, but his feet on solid granite under water, buffeted against the cliff so he could scarce breathe. Mal was there beside him, gripping the same jut of stone. The boy let go of Mal and Mal let go of the boy so they could pull themselves up with both hands safely.

Faced into the cliff, the boy would've just heard the crash of waves ringing in his ears. Deafening it would've been – I know, I've been there – the booming sound echoing from rock wall to rock wall and into the caves and crevasses like the deep groan of a ruined god. Wouldn't have heard Mal's cry in the wind and water. Wouldn't have seen him slipping back behind him, swept off his feet by the rip. Wouldn't have felt the empty space in the air beside him. Would've had his eyes on the girl, on the cliff, on the gulls wheeling above, on the path to safety.

Would've thought they'd made it just in time.

But when he did look back – before he reached the child sprawled on the couch-grass whipped from side to side, leaves like tiny daggers, and the sea pinks swept flat and dancing up in every blast of the storm – when he did look back, Mal wasn't there.

They found the girl stiff and cold on the hillside next morning, her fingernails dug deep into the sandy soil and the grasses, she'd tried so hard to cling on to her life. They found the boy on a ledge halfway down the cliff, his head smashed, where he must have lost his footing trying to climb the rocks in the dark to get help. They found the boat, or leastways, parts of the splintered hull and the snapped oars, snagged on rocks in the lee of the cliff. They didn't find Mal for days, not there neither, not till his body had floated out and back on the tides that washed him up down Newlyn way. He was bloated and blackened with his eyes wide open – though the fishes had one of them – and a triumphant terrible grin on his face.

I pause, often, on the brow of the cliff. I stop and look down at that path – the one Mal took, where I couldn't follow to give him a hand. I remember how, two years before, it was Mal who pulled me out of the water, all broken, and carried me home. I gaze out to sea where his body had floated, the spring clouds reflected as grave green patches on calm grey water. Then I turn my chair and wheel myself away.

LEMON DROP

Clare Howdle

NOUK RUNS. Her calves pull tight and her trainers fill up. This is not the way it's meant to feel, she thinks as her feet sink deeper into the pavement. And yet this is how it always is now.

Four weeks, six days have gone by since the storm hit. Its impact is still being felt. Mounds of sand stretch across Swanpool Road. It drifts and clings. The path around the lake is flooded because sand has clogged the drains. The banks are suffocated and the emptiness it creates bows under its own weight. No ducks flapping. No seagulls fighting over breadcrumbs left for swans by walkers. No moorhens cackling or water rats shooting into the arching roots that a month ago freely tiptoed across the water's edge.

She cranks her music louder and tries to pick up pace, but the sand saps her energy. As the road takes her closer to the sea, the wind throws up clouds of sand. It stings her skin, makes her eyes itch. With every breath, a gritty layer coats her teeth. She sweeps her tongue around her mouth trying to force it out. It crunches and grinds. She has to stop to spit. By the time she reaches the beach, her legs buckle and her rib cage can't keep up. She bends double and pushes her fists into her waist. Her hot breath is whipped away into the brackish air.

Back at the house all she can see is sand. When she shuts her eyes, holds a glass under the tap, listens to the water running, it's there. Stubborn mountains claiming everything from the café terrace to the mini golf course to the new-builds that skirt the back of the lake. She pictures the plants beneath it, bare branches not yet woken up by spring, lost buds dead on the stem. All snuffed out by the choking sand.

'Jesus Christ Nouk, you're so bleak.'

Jonathan's frying bacon. He's got the heat too low. The sizzle is pathetic.

'But isn't it weird though? How no one's doing anything?'

'Not really. What does it matter? It's just sand.'

'They haven't even tried to move it.' Nouk sips her water and lifts herself up onto the counter. She puts her phone down, Gordon Lightfoot still tinny in her earbuds.

'How can you run to that?' he says, shaking his head.

She shrugs and flicks it off.

'You're reading too much into it, anyway,' he prods the rashers in the pan. 'It'll sort itself out eventually. Two or three bits?'

She doesn't answer, watches as he flips the bacon over. It slithers off his spatula with a flaccid wriggle.

'This bloody hob.'

'Have you turned it right up?'

'I know how to fry bacon, Nouk. Get the ketchup, would you?'

He pokes the rashers with a finger and wipes it on his chest. He's still wearing the t-shirt he slept in. His boxers droop around his legs. Nouk taps her socked foot against the cupboard. Under her fingernails, grains have gathered. She picks up a fork and runs a tine along each of them in turn, hooking out the sand and letting it fall onto the side. The pile builds, taking her mind back to the beach.

The storm has reshaped the tideline. Seaweed sits belligerent in fly-ridden heaps, reef newly exposed where the sand has been dragged away. She reaches out to touch the fresh rock, slides her fingers past the razor-like edges and finds purchase between the strata. Her breath rises and falls with the waves.

Running the same route back down the sand road, her lungs thicken.

Jonathan clears his throat sharply, returning her to the kitchen's steamed up windows, the barely spitting pan. He wraps a tea towel around its handle and carries it to the table, where white bread lies buttered. He shakes the pan so some of the bacon stutters onto the thickly cut slices, then squeezes out ketchup in a wheezing gust. 'Help yourself,' he shouts back through to her as he walks into the lounge.

She used to love their weekend mornings. The laziness of not unfolding the day until the afternoon. Lying with her head in Jonathan's lap, both still in their pyjamas, both smelling a little of each other and neither minding. The coffee endlessly brewing, the grease stains on the corners of the paper, his fingers idly curling through her hair. Now he makes bacon sandwiches she can't bring herself to eat. The thought clags and sticks to the roof of her mouth. She wants to say something. To explain why she's running so much or why the sand bothers her or why it would be better if he could just get dressed, rather than loafing around in his boxers pushing ten o'clock in the morning. She wants to tell him why she listens to Gordon Lightfoot. Or Nick Drake. How you can hear them hurting in every word and what better thing is there to run from than that? But she knows he'll just roll his eyes again and maybe call her 'silly girl' then talk about putting dishwasher salt on the shopping list, or that he needs to swing by the office later, okay? He'll pull her to him, and she'll smell his sour sleep smell and taste the sticky, sweet grease and ketchup on his breath. She picks up her trainers and goes upstairs.

They're in the car working around the sequence of roundabouts that takes traffic out of town and onto the ring road. Nouk winds down the window. The cold air feels good. Jonathan mimes a shiver, presses the button in his door handle and winds her window back up.

The homecoming lunch had been in their calendar for nearly a month. Nouk forgot about it until Wednesday when her mother phoned to remind her.

'Alice is going to be woozy of course,' she'd said, her voice lifting to overpower the noisy churn of a mixer. Nouk pictured her, phone squeezed between ear and shoulder, cake batter whipping in the bowl. 'It's not lunchtime for her body. I'm just saying you'll need to take care around her, that's all.'

'Jetlag isn't a disease, Mum. She can suck it up,' Nouk said back.

'I hope you're not going to be in one of your moods, Anoushka,' her mother sighed. 'Please don't ruin it for everyone.' Then she was silent. Then she hung up.

Nouk knows her sister won't be woozy and won't need anyone taking care around her. Instead, she'll be puffed up and proud, telling stories about her internship buddies at the gallery in Upper East Side. How one time after work they sat on bleachers in Sheep's Meadow eating warm pretzels while they watched a rom-com being shot. How after that they hit a dive bar in Hell's Kitchen where she got in on a fake ID and ordered a cocktail called the Lemon Drop that popped in her mouth as she drank. Nouk has heard the stories a hundred times already, pulling on her pyjamas and nodding and smiling while Alice slicked on mascara in the webcam, drooling at the prospect of eggs over easy and biscuits at Bubby's – Tribeca not Highline – where she was meeting 'the gang' for a late brunch.

They pick up speed on the main road as it carries them into open countryside. Jonathan taps his fingers on the wheel, switches presets on the radio, bites the edge of his thumb. She couldn't stop him coming. She tried. The more she protested that she was fine to go alone, the more he'd rubbed his hands on her arms as if warming her up after a cold swim, lunging down so he could look under his eyebrows at her. 'I'll be there,' he said in a hushed, low voice. 'I'll be there.' And now he's winding up her window and turning the radio from Four to Two because it's hard to get into the afternoon plays and Jeremy Vine is pretty funny, actually.

Nouk sits on her hands and clenches her thighs together. She concentrates on what's happening outside the window, searching for the edge of town, where suburbia bleeds out into countryside and the world goes fully wild again. The last of the roofs rushes past the window. The lanes drop from three to two, to one, concrete giving way to granite, bracken. Occasionally they pass a ruined engine house, collapsing walls and chimneys stark against the sky. She winds the window down again and breathes deeply. Jonathan sighs.

'What?' Nouk asks, though she doesn't want to know.

'Nothing I suppose.' He indicates, sighs again, turns the wheel, checks the mirror, sighs louder.

'You didn't have to come,' she says.

'It's not that.'

'Then what?'

He makes a croaking noise in the back of his throat, like the words can't find the shape to take. 'I don't know why we're even going,' he mutters eventually.

'They're my family.'

'All the more reason not to go. You don't even like them – so why waste your weekend? Just tell them the truth, tell them you'd rather not spend your Sunday with them.'

'Because that's what you'd do?'

'My family is not your family.' He clicks his tongue against his teeth, reaches over to squeeze her thigh. 'Everyone deserves the truth, Nouk.'

He says it like he's offering her the advice she's been seeking, a soft lilt to his words.

She punches her consonants back at him, staccato. 'Do you deserve the truth then?'

'What do you mean?'

Across the bay, gulls crowd the back of a fishing trawler, white flecks against a skillet sky. In the distance, strands of darkness fall from the clouds to the sea, sweeping in fast. The boat doesn't stand a chance. He's waiting for Nouk to speak. She stares at the horizon. She knows that to make the lunch bearable she should take it back, but she can't because she has nothing to give him in its place.

A minute later hail attacks. Golf ball sized chunks pummel the bonnet and roof, echoing through the hollow shell of the car.

'Bloody brilliant,' Jonathan shouts, as they pull up outside the house. He flips down the mirror and furiously tousles his hair. Nouk turns away from him, unclicks her seatbelt and leans her forehead against the window. She feels the vibrations of the downpour ripple through her as her breath covers then fades away from the glass.

'It is brilliant,' she says into the thundering hail, so only the storm can hear her.

Nouk's father smiles as he strokes her mother's arm. Long slow brushes back and forth. He's listening to Alice talk, absorbing it all to retell at their next dinner party; how his youngest came good and found herself in New York. He joins in occasionally too, recollecting his own youth and the times they had, every now and then throwing a conspiratorial grin towards his wife.

'–it's so full of life, don't you think?' Alice says about a block sale she stumbled on in Caroll Gardens after visiting the soda fountain where they invented egg cream. She's wearing a charm bracelet she picked up there for a dollar. It jangles as she talks.

'You should have been there in the '90s, Ali' Nouk's father replies. 'Now that was living on the wild side!'

In the past, Nouk and Jonathan might have joked about her father after a lunch like this. How he was a bit pathetic, trying to impress everyone. How the only time he went to New York was with the family and they all stayed with his brother near Larchmont and only drove into the city twice. They might have done impressions of him, making up increasingly ludicrous places and events he claimed to be a part of. Nouk might have ended up burying her face in the bedsheets to smother out the hilarity of it, noticing Jonathan's touch getting more urgent as he massaged her side, his face suddenly serious and purposeful. She looks at Jonathan forking potatoes into his mouth, nodding and smiling at her father, at Alice. It's like they're in a different world now.

Alice is talking about the rom-com in Central Park again. Nouk's father is still brushing her mother's forearm, as if he's charging a balloon up for a static shock. Nouk's mother half smiles through tight lips, her eyes locked on the cutlery neatly pushed together on her plate. She doesn't lift his hand away, or stroke his arm back, or cup her fingers over his in affection. There's no indication she can feel it at all.

Nouk thinks back to the car and Jonathan's broken face when she jabbed her question at him. Each little word daring him to respond, ready to bite back if he did, so they could get it all out in the open. Although she knew he wouldn't. She trusted in it. A safety net, baggy and worn, but with just enough tension left in it to hold. He talks about telling the truth like it's so simple to untangle, she thinks. Like anyone can. That's when she feels it. In the middle of one of her father's anecdotes about a kid spitting off the Empire State Building. Jonathan's hand, on her arm. Stroke. Stroke. Stroke.

Nouk clocks off work at midnight. She weaves a path between the drunks outside the kebab shop. Someone shouts something leery at her, so she cuts down a snicket onto the waterfront, where it's quieter. The sky is clear after another day of heavy rain and the quayside is slick with milk-white light. When she reaches the pier, she sits, taking a breather before climbing the steep high street home. Reflections on the water make the world dance. Moored boats sway, the wind spinning their masts into a song of wire against metal. With no trawlers to chase, the gulls wheel above the bins, swoop to yank out wrappers and hiss over whatever they find.

She pulls her coat tight around her, thinks about her shift. About the pint she pulled for the lecturer whose name she doesn't know but whose face she recognises. He drinks there a lot. Often, he smiles at her. Tonight, he said something funny, and she laughed. He laughed too. It made her skin prickle. It's prickling again now, and she focuses on it, lets it warm her against the chill of the midnight air. She slouches down on the bench, closes her eyes and embraces the glimmer of possibility – how a look, a movement, could fill her so entirely for a moment, making everything else slide away. And it's not about something happening. It's not about him, or the way his hand brushed the edge of hers as she passed him his pint. The curiosity of what if and the excitement it carries would quickly die if it went any further, replaced by guilt and confusion and the crippling normality of it all. It's just the potential she finds herself clinging to, more powerful than reality and more hopeful than truth. It pops like she imagines a Lemon Drop might. It makes her feel alive.

Her teeth chatter. There's pressure in her chest pushing the air from her body. Behind her closed eyelids she sees the moon blazing.

Nouk wakes just before six, frozen. The sun is beginning to turn everything grey. She pulls her collar up and ducks her mouth inside her coat to warm her body with her breath. Two seagulls peck at a crisp packet in front of her. Across the estuary, more gulls murmur skyward as boats silently ghost their way out to sea.

Jonathan will want an explanation. To know where she was and why she didn't call. She could pretend she was with someone. That all this time her distraction, her spikiness has been because she is cheating on him. He would nod, tight-lipped as he turned the last few weeks over, seeing how her behaviour slotted neatly into that reality. He would look hurt and sad and lost, but wouldn't feel the need to say sorry, or that he'll try harder. They wouldn't have to hold hands or talk in circles and fail to find a way out. A simple lie, over a complicated truth. It would make things much easier for both of them.

Swanpool Lake is in the opposite direction to home. By the time Nouk gets there the morning is bright and full. Her cheeks warm in the light. There's no wind and where the road curves along the front she can see lazy waves licking the shore. She sits on the storm drain that joins the lake to the sea and watches the freshwater surge down the grill, through salty rocks then into the open ocean. She pictures the fish beneath the surface, swimming frantically against the suck and pull, attempting to stay where they are but up against forces far more powerful. Through the rusty grate, down the pipe, spat into the sea – what happens next? Do they celebrate the surprise of their newfound freedom, a whole ocean to explore? Or do they drown in the salt water because it's too much for their freshwater gills to take?

Either side of the drain, the displaced storm sand rears up in heaps, covering what used to be nettles, blackberry bushes, hawthorn and birch. She digs her fingers in deep, feels the wet, dense resistance of the sand under her nails. Her hands linger for a moment in the cool, still smother of it, before she begins to dig.

She works slowly at first then faster, harder, scooping great handfuls away and piling it at her feet.

The deeper she burrows, the more difficult the sand is to move. Compacted, wet, resistant. She speeds up, gouges with her nails, leans over, reaches in. Something in her demands it; compels her to get to the bottom, to get rid. The hole she makes gapes, a dark mouth swallowing her body with every pull and claw. Her shoulders ache with the effort. Sweat beads up along her hairline, cold kisses on the back of her neck.

Suddenly, it's there. A survivor. The tiniest tip of a pencil-thin branch sticks out where she's digging, then another, then another. She holds her breath, her fervour tempered by the tree's delicacy, its dependence on what she does next. She teases her fingers under the branches to work them loose, cups her hands around each one like they are flames in a breeze, protecting them from the crumbling walls of the hole as she gently lifts and goads more of the tree free. As soon as they're released, the branches spring up, bendy new green against the blue sky. Life, Nouk thinks. Even under the weight of all that. Even in the darkness and uncertainty, not knowing if it would ever break through. Life.

She falls back onto the sand and wipes the sweat from her forehead in a gritty sweep. The tree stands proud in the daylight. Above her, clouds drift. She hears shingle clack as the tide drags over the shore. The call of gulls. Birdsong. There's the fast thump of a dog's feet pounding across the beach after a ball. An early, eager family playing by the water. Nouk gets up, dusts the sand off her hands and turns towards the road that leads back home. On the very edge of her vision, the little tree dances in the breeze.

BOSCREGAN

Tim Martindale

IT WAS autumn, and there were few trees for shelter on the exposed, south-west peninsula in Cornwall that is known as Penwith; only the small, stunted woods that cling to the steep valleys where streams cut their way to the sea. The season was marked by a succession of gales and rain-battered days, occasionally lifted by the odd fresh and luminescent day with the cliffs bathed in sunshine, gulls and fulmars flying low over the waves out at sea, chasing the shoals of mackerel that come in with the swells. One rather more murky morning, I walked down onto Botallack cliffs through the old mine workings to do a litter-pick in the *mizzle* – that peculiarly Cornish blend of fine rain and mist that can hang over the coast and moors for days at a time, till it becomes hard to tell where land and sea begin and end.

It was early on in my new job as a ranger, based at a National Trust site at Botallack, near St Just, helping to look after an area of coastline which stretches from Land's End to the village of Pendeen on the north coast. A rugged stretch of cliffs, old mine workings, small farms, coves and villages of low granite houses, sandwiched between the sea and the brooding massif of the moors that runs down through the spine of Penwith. As I descended that morning below the line of fog, the heather-clad cliffs and twin mine engine-houses known as 'the Crowns' perched on the edge far below came into clear view, seemingly empty and forsaken of people. The low winter sun that was now dipping below the clouds cast a luminous grey-gold light over the ocean where gannets dived.

Following a random path down the cliff face, I stumbled across the entry to the Cargodna mine shaft, where a memorial commemorates the Wheal Owles disaster. On 10th January 1893, about forty men and boys were underground when the shaft flooded with water. The mine surveyor had used old mine charts and had failed to account for magnetic declination (the variation of magnetic north over time), throwing his calculations out. They had excavated into an old, flooded shaft running adjacent to Cargodna. Nineteen men and a boy were killed, and their bodies remain in the mine to this day. As I walked on along the cliff path, I imagined voices here, spirits of the dead, miners entombed in their sea-girt graves, in tunnels that lay under my feet in these cliffs and out under the sea, voices filling this realm where only they and the seagulls cry. Exploring the warren of paths and lanes, sheltered in places by overgrown stone hedges, it wasn't hard to imagine how, not so long ago, weary miners once trod the same paths on their way home to St Just and other nearby villages, after their shift of long, dark and hot hours toiling below ground. I felt sure they must have found some comfort in the small birds darting between hedges that in spring and summer would have been full of evening song.

Although the history of this place felt, at times like this, almost tangible in the sea mist-laden air and the lichen-clad granite stone ruins of the mines, it is a history that I couldn't claim any close personal connection to. I'd grown up in Cornwall, but not in Penwith. Mine was a rural upbringing, but on small farms further east and inland – the son of a farmer, not a fisherman or a miner, and for the majority of my childhood, brought up by my mum, a social worker, and my stepdad, a stone mason. I left at eighteen to go to university in London and had periodically come back, as a juvenile peregrine will return to the place of its birth long after having fledged, until it has firmly established a territory of its own. This latest return had been presaged by the breakdown of a long-term relationship, followed by a painful love affair, and a struggle to find direction and stability in life after the completion of a long period of academic study. Instead, I was caught up in that common trap of people today in their twenties and thirties and without means – of high rent and low-paid and relatively unfulfilling labour. But probably the roots of the pervasive anxiety and lack of confidence that shadowed me stemmed back to long before all that.

Seeking a fresh start, I left my job as a bookseller in a small town in Sussex nestled in the South Downs. It was a place where I had only just begun to build a new life after running away from London, and one which I had a growing affection for. Yet I was acutely aware I had no history or roots there, no deep-rooted familial bond to the landscape around me. And this was something I had a profound longing for.

Having returned to Cornwall, the chance of a job working for the National Trust as a ranger seemed like just the opportunity I was looking for: to reconnect and ground myself, to find a new path – one in which my connection to the landscape around me might be less a cerebral, romantic and nostalgia-riddled one, instead grounded in the practical skills and knowledge of how to look after and care for the land and for nature. It was to prove a difficult journey. It isn't always easy to return to a place of origin, especially with complex family relationships and troubled histories to navigate. Living in a caravan on my dad's farm, with only this temporary job to hold me above water, I was aware of the precariousness of my position should things not work out.

So far, the job hadn't been quite all I had imagined it to be. There was the long list of relatively mundane maintenance tasks that had been neglected since my predecessor went on long-term sick leave. Then there had been the ominous threats made on social media against staff and volunteers by one or two extreme locals. An atmosphere of mistrust had developed around the National Trust's presence and work here, especially since the filming of Poldark. The latest TV series, in which the Crowns in particular featured as a prominent backdrop, had brought many more visitors to the area, but had also aggravated some locals, who believed that the National Trust was an outside corporate intrusion on the place, seeking to 'cash in' on the area's history and natural beauty.

In the early days of my relatively brief ranger apprenticeship, this atmosphere of conflict only served to exacerbate my sense of alienation and *un*belonging, the opposite of what I had come back to Cornwall to seek. However, part of my role as a ranger, and of the National Trust more generally, was to help conserve not only the wildlife and ecology of the area, but also the distinctive material remains of its history, written like a palimpsest in the network of ancient pathways and stone boundaries that crisscross the landscape. Not only markers of history; careful upkeep of these features enables visitors and locals alike to continue to form and maintain their own connection with the land. Helping to repair them would become my way of forming a bond with it too.

Many of the hedges in Penwith date back to the Bronze Age and are older than the Egyptian Pyramids. Others are more recent, having been thrown up by miners who were often also small-scale farmers. Some of these are over six feet high and built with huge boulders at waist and even shoulder height. I had to marvel at the strength and technique it took to get them up there without mechanical assistance. Some were dry-stone walls, others built in the traditional Cornish style, typically from granite with a core of earth in the middle. This is what distinguishes a Cornish 'hedge' from a stone 'wall', as found in other parts of the country, such as Yorkshire and the Lake District. The earthen core not only binds the stone but becomes a seedbed for trees, shrubs and flowers, so that in time it becomes a living hedge, home for many plants and animals.

My interest in Cornish hedging had begun seven or so months previously as a full-time volunteer ranger working at Godolphin, a historic estate east of the Hayle River. There I had discovered a love for working with stone, repairing hedges that formed the field boundaries and that had collapsed in places – under the weight of a fallen tree, livestock, or just time and weather. After a long estrangement, I had reconnected with my stepfather, a stonemason and quarryman, who ran a business supplying fine architectural granite. Hearing of my new-found passion and my need for some cash to support my volunteering he set me up with his friend Mark, an expert Cornish hedger who agreed to take me under his wing. In return for my help and in the little time we had while I was labouring one day a week for him, he taught me what he could of the craft.

A small, quiet, but energetic man, in his mid-sixties I guessed, Mark seemed to me to resemble the sparrows that flitted around his yard at my stepfather's quarry. He fed the birds every day, whistling to gather them to him, throwing some seed amongst the old pieces of granite he was collecting – milling stones, bird baths, cattle troughs, some dating back to medieval times. An ex-miner, I quickly learnt that Mark was a humble and principled character – a lover, like my stepfather, of nature, of old things and values, of hard work, history, heritage, and craftsmanship, of friendship and helping one another out, putting people before money. On my first day out with him we drove around the narrow Cornish lanes in his small flatbed builder's van, looking at examples of hedging that he thought were particularly well-constructed and others that he thought were bad. It wasn't just that a Cornish hedge should have a gently concave face, wide at the bottom, tapering in towards the middle, before gently widening again towards the top. The outward facing stones should be clean and flush with each other, tightly packed with earth and with no holes or gaps. Longer 'key stones' should be laid with the length going back into the hedge to give it strength.

As pleasant as these days out with Mark were, they were also days of persistent, low-level frustration, like working on a giant jigsaw puzzle, picking through piles of stone, trying to find the perfectly shaped one to fit next to the ones already laid, struggling to learn fast enough to meet my own and Mark's high expectations. Yet I found the flow and pattern of it calmed my mind, typically prone to anxiety. I could lose myself in total, focused attention on the task at hand. And I enjoyed being with Mark working on a hedge in some quiet out-of-the-way spot. We'd have our tea and packed lunches (or 'crib' as he called it, using the old miners' term) sitting in his van, and we found a common interest in history. He was a gentle and good-natured chap, and I felt privileged that he agreed to take the time to try and teach me what he knew.

Knowing of my enthusiasm for hedging, the Lead Ranger asked me to lead a project to repair a section of hedge on a tenant farm, and in the process share the skills I was learning with some of the younger volunteer rangers. Working alone one weekend morning, as my role often entailed, I drove the Land Rover out across the fields of Boscregan, a remote farm that looked out to sea between Cape Cornwall and Land's End, with Bob Marley playing loud on the stereo. Earlier in the week, I had been out there working with a couple of the volunteers. As much as I enjoyed their company and questions, teaching them the modest amount I had learnt about hedging, it was trying sometimes to get them to stop chatting and larking around, and instead to focus on the work at hand. I was looking forward to cracking on with the job on my own for the day.

The fields had been sown with an arable crop and allowed to go to seed to provide food for the birds. The crop was interspersed with weeds and wildflowers such as corn marigolds, a riot of colour in spring and early summer, but now nodding lifelessly in the autumn sea breeze. A monotone of pale gold and browns under a low grey sky, to a casual observer's eye it might have looked as if the farm had been allowed to go to wrack and ruin, gradually being overcome by nature again. But this was all part of the Trust's conservation management plan for this tenant farm. Buzzards and kestrels soared, hovered, and dived in the sky around me as I worked. Unfortunately, the stone hedges had also been long neglected and allowed to go to ruin by the tenant farmer, as the hooves of cattle climbing the hedges to reach more inviting grass on the other side gradually took their toll. The stone we were using for the repairs was a mixture of reclaimed granite from around the farm and some we had brought in from further afield, all Penwith stone. Some of the stone on site was of the quality known as *growan*, a local dialect term for decomposed granite, especially common in Penwith, for here the granite has often lain on or close to the surface of the ground for a very long time, exposed to the eroding action of the weather. Some of it was so crumbly that we could practically break it apart with bare hands or a tap of the lump hammer. It was ideal for using in the core of the hedge, alongside earth.

The fields ran right to the cliff-edge, to the headland where long-horned cattle grazed, and the surf curled and broke. Later that morning, the weather began to roll in, a thick sea mist that became heavier and more persistent till it became rain, enclosing me in my own little world. With the roar of the surf, it was almost as if I was at sea, and I felt nauseous and sick with it. That, and an undefined anxiety, as I slipped around in the mud, attempting to heave the big *grounder* stones into place (the boulders that would provide the foundation for the hedge). The wet and weathered rock tore at my hands as I went backwards and forwards with my wheelbarrow of earth to backfill the hedge, tamping in the soil around the stones with the butt of my lump hammer. Eventually I was forced to take shelter in the Land Rover, and I had my tea and sandwiches as the rain ran down the windscreen. I texted my girlfriend Nika, who lived far away in Sussex, to tell her how much I was missing her. Our relationship, still tender and new, had sprung up since I had moved away from Sussex and returned to Cornwall, but already I felt keenly her absence between visits. Receiving a heartfelt message in return, I found tears running down my face. How far away she felt and how I longed to have her beside me, to be able to share all this wild and raw beauty with her, even on a day like today.

After lunch, the work began to flow better, and I found a rhythm and a calm as I took pleasure in finding the stone that would fit just right next to the one laid before. The weather was beginning to clear too. I lost track of time and after a couple of hours, I stopped to rest and have another cup of tea, finding a grassy spot to sit and lean against the old, rambling hedge. Before me lay a silver, mist-shrouded sea, sunlight moving across the waves, and the string of rocks that jutted out from the sea, known as the Longships, fading into obscurity. A buzzard seemed to hover over the fallow corn crop and the dead marigolds. Had he learnt to do this from the kestrels, one of which hovered nearby, I wondered.

That day, my body and will pushed against stone, until some internal resistance in me was overcome, and I was free to receive these gifts, the mystery of this place, waves cresting the Longships and spotlights of sun searching the grey sea. My eyes and ears searched too, picking out a tumble of stones on the headland – a cairn or Iron Age cliff castle, a deer grazing in a neighbouring field, the mewing cries of a family of buzzards. Suddenly I felt whole again, resistance and struggle turning to acceptance: of my tumultuous feelings that day and of the person I was, someone in whom excitement often coexists with anxiety, in whom an earthy self, needing a tactile and physical connection to nature and the outdoors, cohabits with a more intellectual and creative self. So often in the past I had struggled to reconcile these different parts of myself, but now I knew they were part of an organic whole, with a common origin in the life that led back, via these ancient stones being reused in the landscape, to my stonemason stepdad and his quarry, to the smallholding where I grew up, to my mum and her love of literature, her passion, intellect and wit, to my dad, a farmer, and his love of history and of the land. All these streams and rivers running through a person, like the lodes of precious minerals that Cornishmen and women have chased through the hard granite that persists and goes on forever, living its different lives, but always remaining in essence the same.

How strange a thing, to feel love for a hedge, I thought. To stand back again and again, admire how snugly the stones fit, how the shadowed lines between them meet and flow, how each stone and the hedge as a whole belongs in this landscape, as much as the *kee-kee* of the buzzard, the kestrel hovering perfectly still into a keen wind, the hardy cattle and the granite farmhouse that bears the wind and rain.

The mist had cleared now, and the late afternoon light was beautiful. I packed up my tools and walked around 'the Gribba', as the headland is called, where a group of choughs wheeled and spun in 360 degree turns, eschewing their distinctive, clattering call as they cruised by. Once commonplace in Cornwall, this small black bird with a red beak, similar in size and of the same corvid family as the rook and the jackdaw, had until relatively recently all but disappeared, with only a few breeding pairs clinging on in remote parts of Wales. Now they are gradually returning to the Cornish coast, with colonies establishing themselves in a few remote spots, including Rinsey, Lizard Point and Botallack. Swooping around the mines and cliffs, cloaked with the aura of myth and mystery that has accumulated around them, associations with King Arthur, Merlin and the Celts, they were a joy to behold.

I looked down to the beach below, littered by huge, round, white rocks like dinosaur eggs, and along the towering cliffs – steep stacks of angular, wave-cut stone – swearing under my breath at the beauty of it all. Back inland across the golden arable fields, the farmstead of grey and brown-hued granite was aglow in the evening sun, glinting off the Land Rover where I had left it in the field. Beyond, small green parcels of land stretched away across the valley. This is what it is to care for a place, I thought, this dilapidated farm and twenty-first century refuge for wildlife, the essence or spirit of it unchanging, even as the old forms of culture and community have changed or have fallen away forever.

THE FATE OF T VASILY 03

Elaine Ruth White

'THEY SAY no one can hear a scream in the vacuum of space.'

The kneeling Transient's voice tremored, betraying his desperation. Karim didn't look at him. Neither did he look at his fellow warder but knew there would be a sneering smirk of delight lurking behind an assumed veneer of compassion. He'd seen it seven times before. Witnessed Bonnar's insistence on this ridiculous, pointless ritual designed to drag out the inevitable suffering. Karim hated the squirming sensation his bowels made when, before, he'd watched the alternating flashes of terror and hope cross inmates' faces. He'd learned to look away, to look at a point just above their heads, to study the deep space sky outside, with its flickering remnants of beginnings and endings. He'd learned to keep his gaze at such a discrete angle Bonnar would never guess he wasn't watching. Karim knew what would happen if Bonnar even suspected he was giving in to any kind of lily-livered response. But still, the whimper in the inmate's voice reminded him of the times when he had watched and found himself almost admiring Bonnar's tremendous sense of sadistic timing.

'Close, but no cigar. Time's ticking.' Bonnar trilled the last word. *Tiiii... kiiing.*

'Please, forgive me. I had so little time to spend in the Archives. Work, family, I barely had time to sleep some days. And the Archives are so vast.'

'You know what they say, knowledge is currency. Trust me, it's a well-known…' Bonnar snapped his fingers in Karim's direction. 'What's the word I'm wanting here?'

'Aphorism?' Karim offered.

'Exactly. It's a well-known one of those. And the quote is, like, well famous. From one of the great William Shakespeare's most famous movies.'

Karim closed his eyes for a nano-second longer than a blink, desperate to shut out the staggering depth of Bonnar's ignorance. If knowledge was currency, Bonnar was bankrupt. His gaze returned to the spot just above the inmate's freshly shaven head, with its nicks from a too sharp razor and its Cho Ku

Rei tattoo, the latter a power symbol believed to help its wearer face great challenges. Karim didn't need to ask what this man's challenge had been. He could guess.

The Transient's eyes darted left to right, up and down, as if their searching might reveal the answer to Bonnar's question, written on the gleaming titanium inner walls of the airlock. His tongue flicked, trying to moisten lips that were so dry they stuck together.

'In space…'

'That's good. Keep it coming.'

The Transient's breath came quicker, his bony chest rising and falling beneath the thin, torn calico shirt.

'In space, they say, no one can hear a scream.'

'Nearly there! Nearly there!'

Bonnar's huge frame bounced up and down in an almost childish delight, but at the same time, one meaty hand moved closer to the console left of the outer airlock door. He knew the answer would be in the Archive. It wasn't his fault if the Transient had been too lazy to learn.

The Archive had been created to give Transients a genuine opportunity to progress. It had instantaneous translation into every known language in existence, the highest-grade search facility yet developed, and a phenomenal bank of subject matter updated on an hourly basis. The goal had been to enable every

Transient to become a valued, equal member of society. It had taken generations to finally accept there was never going to be a Final Solution to put an end to the perpetual global migration; to stem the insistent drive to find a better life. A radical new vision was needed. For too long, people had been economically segregated, categorised in terms of consumer groups, with Transients at the bottom of the heap, particularly those considered to be illegals. They'd been labelled parasites, outcasts punished by a cat's cradle of bureaucratic legislation preventing them becoming valuable, contributing members of their chosen society, all in the vain hope this would, in some magical way, discourage the people trade by undermining the business model of the traffickers. Years wasted in the fruitless pursuit of genuine human progress based on profit and loss accounts. Years wasted in the dehumanising belief that every problem could be solved if enough money was thrown at it, a facile attempt by the ruling elite to be seen to tackle a human crisis. Those who devised the Vision had seen past the blinkered, mercenary relationships that had come to dominate all areas of existence. The aim of the Vision was to move forward to a world where compassion, empathy, and the value of all human knowledge were placed on a pedestal adjacent and equal to profit. Environmental, social and governance departments were no longer poor governing bedfellows, but guiding lights. It was to meet corporate ESG requirements that had led to the development of the deep space stations, new worlds devoted to promoting the well-being of Transients. In the beginning there had been fertile opposition. It was argued the Stations replicated the lunatic asylums of the 19th century, which had only further undermined well-being by creating a trapped and institutionalised populace. Others saw it as a backdoor attempt to reprise the creation of brave new worlds that, in reality, were nothing more than penal colonies. But early fears had proved to be unfounded. The Stations had seen Transients receive the input they needed to genuinely progress. To go on to the safer, better lives they had craved. If they were prepared to learn.

Yes, knowledge is currency, mused Karim, but what happened to those who wouldn't, or couldn't, learn. Or share that learning.

'Okay, last chance.' Bonnar was in his element. He'd grasped the gist of allowing all to progress through the Elevation of Knowledge, but somehow the ethos behind it – and the compassion – had completely eluded him.

Karim heard the Transient start muttering and then emit a guttural sound more animal than human. Against his better instincts, he glanced down.

The Transient's hands were locked together in a gesture of prayer. Was that instinctive? Genetic memory? It was certainly no longer taught. Hadn't been since the Vision was implemented. The man's lips trembled, his head shaking from side to side, eyes locked on Bonnar.

Despite himself, Karim began to will the man to give Bonnar the right answer. He pictured the words travelling across space from his mind to the Transient's. He saw large black letters penetrate the airlock door and swirl around the Transient's head.

Look around you, Karim exhorted silently. See the words. In your mind's eye. See them.

The Transient tore his gaze from Bonnar and looked toward Karim. His babbling stopped. His lips began to move purposefully.

'In space...' he began, 'In space, no one can hear you...'

Bonnar slammed his fist against the console. The outer airlock door flew open, and the Transient was gone.

'Did you hear that? On the comms?' Bonnar beamed triumphantly. 'I swear he screamed. Right as the airlock opened. Did you hear it? I heard it. Swear I did. Right, my friend, I think we've earned ourselves a right royal breakfast.' Bonnar turned sharply on his heel and headed for the linking corridor that led to his breakfast. After a guilt-tinged glance at the airlock that had just ejected Transient Vasily 03, Karim followed.

All the eating facilities on the Station were excellent – progress marches on its stomach – and the one thing Karim and Bonnar agreed upon was that the canteen on D deck was without doubt the best. The head chef, Mo, a Transient woman in her 80s originally from the Far-Lands, had been a total knowledge freak most of her life, and catering excellence had followed. There was always a theme, usually a celebration with a dark or humorous twist, built around historical events found on the Archive.

Today was no exception.

A banner hung from the ceiling with the tongue-in-cheek declaration: EARTH: REFERENDUM VOTES TO LEAVE SOLAR SYSTEM. Menus graced the tables, laid out like news reports referencing the beginning of the Great Break Up and the Third War to End All Wars. Karim got the reference, smiled, and silently applauded the irony. The joke, like the banner, went over Bonnar's head.

'What's good today?'

'*All* is good.' Mo was sensitive to any suggestion her food was ever anything other than top notch. She was a Transient who'd decided to progress as far as she could. She had found her new life and took pride in it.

'He means what's special.'

Karim winked gently at Mo as he spoke. He'd always had a way of diffusing tension, of pouring oil on troubled waters. Once, his way of keeping the peace had helped in the Mid-Lands, but the Third War to End All Wars had changed everything and now, on the Station, it was seen as unnecessary. Nothing seriously interrupted the peace, so there was no need for peacekeepers. It had taken a long time for Karim to adjust. By the time he progressed to the status of Warder, a cushy number given the lack of any meaningful conflict, he had gained much knowledge but had struggled to find his identity in this new world. Six months working with Bonnar had done the rest. After fourteen months on Deep Space Station Kappa, Karim felt emasculated.

'Then he should say that. Special? The mushrooms. A medley. Three varieties. Fresh picked. Tomatoes. Silken tofu. Seeded bread straight from the oven. Heaven on a plate. And nothing needed to die in the process.'

Karim squirmed as the face of the Transient in the airlock pushed its unwelcome way into his mind.

'I eat what I want. Alive or dead. I'm not squeamish.'

Mo regarded Bonnar with contempt.

'That's because you were never a Transient. You

wear your privilege like a close-fitting coat. What can I get you, my friend?' Mo's face softened as she looked at the younger man whom she had seen progress so well, though not necessarily in a direction she approved of.

Karim's stomach churned at the thought of food, even food as good as Mo's, but he was too polite to say.

'Mushrooms sound great.'

'I'll have the works.' Bonnar grunted.

'Of course you will.'

Mo left the sarcasm hanging in the air, turned on her heel, and headed back to the sanctuary of her kitchen. Bonnar gave her back a sour look.

'These Transients are getting above themselves if you ask me.'

It never ceased to amaze Karim how Bonnar would talk about Transients as if Karim wasn't one of them. At first, he thought it was a sign of acceptance and felt reassured. Later though he came to frame it as a refusal to acknowledge him on any significant level at all, unless Bonnar needed a whipping boy. But they'd never discussed it because Bonnar never mentioned it and Karim never brought it up. He just assumed it was likely the latter in the same way as he assumed his progress would continue if he kept up his visits to the Archive, logging his hours like deep sea divers log their time at depth.

'Cat got your tongue?' At the table, Bonnar was starting in on him, out of boredom perhaps, or to release some pent-up tension, but before Karim could answer, a plate of food was waved in front of their faces.

'Mushrooms?'

'Mine.' said Karim, sitting back in his chair as a second plate descended swiftly and landed neatly in front of Bonnar. The server gave a theatrical flourish, like a magician might after successfully tricking a member of the audience, then leant forward, floppy fringe falling across her face, an impish look dancing behind her mock serious expression.

'Cat got your tongue! Did you know that saying goes back over 5000 years? The ancient Egyptians liked to cut out the tongues of blasphemers and feed them to their cats. Cats were worshipped in Egypt. Did you know cats don't have a sweet-tooth and a cat's hairball is called a bezoar? They usually vomit these up, but there are any number of methods to help a cat rid themselves of a hairball. I love cats and there is just so much information about them in the Archives. Do you have a cat? Having a pet can be very therapeutic for your health. A number of medical research trials show that patients in terminal care facilities report far less pain when they have an animal to pet, particularly a cat. Before I became a Transient

– I was still only seven years old – I would visit my grandmother who had a dozen cats. I read of an old lady once who had dozens of cats and when she died, they fed on her body. I learned on the Archive that it was their way of showing love and saying goodbye. Isn't that lovely? Things to consider: do cats really have nine lives, is curiosity lethal, and can cats really be alive and dead at the same time? According to one 20th century physicist, that is entirely possible. Enjoy your meal.'

Karim smiled inside at the outpouring of acquired knowledge. Once, he'd had to work that hard at the Archives. Now he didn't need to, and he was grateful. He still kept up his hours, logging them diligently, but he'd achieved. He could relax. A little.

The young server left, but before either Karim or Bonnar could raise fork to mouth, the internal comms systems coughed into life:

'T Vasily 03. Log in please.'

Karim frowned and looked at Bonnar, who barely hesitated before plunging his knife and fork into his eggs.

'Did you hear that?'

Bonner didn't stop chewing. 'Eat your breakfast.'

'The Transient we just... processed. The system just called for him.'

'So what? Eat up!'

Karim stared at his plate; an uncomfortable lump

had formed in his throat.

'I'm not hungry.'

Bonnar lunged at Karim's plate and loaded his fork with a healthy measure of his colleague's mushrooms.

'Relax. Come on. It's just a job. Let it go. Eat your breakfast.'

'But why did they order it?'

'Why did they order what?'

'Why did they order us to take them. To *lose* them. What makes them different? There have been eight now. Eight in as many days. Why? And why us?'

'Why us? Well, as an old army captain of mine used to say: ours is not to reason why. He said it was good advice he'd received from a Transient who learned it through the Archives but, sadly, failed to act on it.' Bonnar gave a slight snigger. 'Anyway, I like to work on a need-to-know basis. And I don't need to know more than I already told you and that was what they told me.'

'Have they asked other warders to do the same?'

'No one's said anything.'

'It just doesn't fit with everything else they do. Don't you ever ask yourself what's changed?'

'Nothing's changed. They know what they're doing.'

The comms system wheezed again.

'T Vasily 03. Log in please.'

Karim's face paled, then reddened, betraying the fact that he was both unsettled at the insistence the deceased Transient should log in, and irritated by the fact they had on board all the wonders of early 23rd century technology, yet the intercom still sounded like an old man with a respiratory disease. But now the insistent croaking seemed to take on a sinister tone. He felt increasingly nervous.

'But if they asked you, I mean, us, to see to it, why are they now asking him to log in? They never asked the others to log in after… you know. I mean why would they? They've processed hundreds, thousands of Transients. It's always the same. The shuttle arrives. They're deplaned. Processed. Then the learning begins. They start their new lives. End of. Then, out of the wide blue yonder, eight are brought to us, one after the other to… you know. And we do that, no questions asked and no follow up. Then this. They broadcast to the whole Station that they want—' Karim lowered his voice to a whisper '—a *dead* man to log in. It doesn't make sense. What's changed?'

'What does it matter? And why do you care anyway?'

Karim's throat tightened.

'Because it could be me.'

'How could it be you? You're here. You're a Warder enjoying your privileges. Like eating your breakfast.'

Bonnar's cognitive processes were resolutely concrete.

'Okay then, it could be like family. Or a friend.'

Bonnar stopped chewing.

'You have friends who are Transients?'

'Of course.'

'Really? Why?'

The truth struck Karim like a stone: Bonnar doesn't know. Is that possible? And if Bonnar doesn't know, how would he react if he found out? From someone else. Would he think Karim had been deliberately holding out on him? And would he then suspect Karim might be holding out on other things. Maybe Bonnar would look at Karim a little more closely. With suspicion even. That was the last thing Karim wanted. His breath came faster. Should he tell, or not tell? As he sat there, his breakfast chilling on its plate, the Archive's choices and voices churned round in his mind: I'm between a rock and a hard place. Scilla and Charybdis. The hammer and the anvil. The Devil and the deep blue sea. It's a predicament. A bind. A dilemma. Hobson's choice. A no-win.

'Because *I'm* a Transient.' Karim blurted it out.

Bonnar's lower jaw dropped so fast and so low it would have seemed comical under other circumstances.

'You are?'

Karim gave the merest of nods, his eyes never leaving Bonnar's face.

'Do they know?'

'Do they know what?' Karim's wary brow furrowed.

'Do they know you're a Transient?'

'Of course they know. They placed me.'

'They placed you with me?'

'You know they did.'

'Did they tell me?'

'I don't know. Did you ask?'

'I already told you…'

'Yes. Yours is not to reason why.' Karim exhaled what was almost a breath of relief and disbelief.

Then Bonnar threw his arms in the air, knife and fork still clutched in his pudgy fingers.

'A Transient. They expected me to work with a Transient. Not a word or by your leave. How long were you going to hide it?'

'I didn't hide it. I thought you already knew.'

Red-faced, Bonnar looked like he was going to choke on his breakfast. He swallowed hard and was about to spit back a reply when the comms coughed into life again.

'T Vasily 03, log in please.'

For a second Bonnar was distracted. Karim

clutched at the opportunity.

'So what do we do?' I mean, do we tell them what's happened? In case it's a mistake, like an admin error.'

'They don't make mistakes.'

'Everyone makes mistakes.'

'Not them. *They* don't. They *don't.*'

Bonnar was now clenching his fists white-knuckled round his cutlery. Like many not blessed with the ability to articulate well, he expressed his inner conflict much more physically, like a child having a tantrum. Karim could see the tension building in the big man's frame. His shoulders were hunched, his fingers clenching and unclenching. The heel of one foot was tapping repeatedly on the ceramic flooring. Bonnar was starting to draw attention to himself. So Karim did what he did best. He pacified.

'No, you're right. Of course. They don't make mistakes. We probably misread the manifest sheet. Maybe it was T Vasily 01 in that airlock. Or 02. Forget it. Finish your breakfast. Do you want coffee? Maybe some juice? You relax and enjoy. I'll be straight back.'

At the self-serve drinks counter, Karim pretended to stare at the options, thankful to be away from Bonnar's rising fury. He would no doubt have to face the fallout from his revelation in the not-too-distant future, but what troubled him more was the repeated request that had come over the comms. In his mind, he replayed the morning and pictured the manifest. He would stake a month's pay on it reading the name T Vasily 03 under the heading 'For Transit'.

When they had received their first Transit order, Bonnar, as a senior warder, had been told that the person to be moved on presented a severe risk to all those on DSS Kappa. But no explanation was given as to the nature of the risk. There were over 3000 people aboard the Station, so it was hard to envisage what risk one sole individual could pose. When they were presented with a second person the next day, Karim thought perhaps a pair of Transients had begun to share some poisonous discontent – there were always mumblings amongst some, usually about trivial matters that were swiftly dealt with in a sensitive, diplomatic manner, with a post-incident focus group discussion ensuring everything had been resolved to the satisfaction of all. Discontent rarely rumbled on for long. And even if it did, ejection would have been an extreme, and out of proportion response. A punishment, if that's what it was, that did not fit a relatively minor infringement such as dissent. Had they refused to learn? Did that explain their exit? But the ethos decreed that given the right environment, all people would flourish. Daily affirmations received over the comms reinforced the value of working at individual, and therefore community, progress. Of valuing the distance travelled instead of despairing at the distance still to go. Of never giving up. None of that fit with the Transit orders of the past eight days. And T Vasily 03.

Karim forced himself to picture the little man, seemingly inoffensive in every way. He'd never noticed him around the Station, but then, he'd not seemed the type who would stand out. Just an ordinary Joe. Except for the tattoo. The power symbol. That would have attracted attention if it hadn't been hidden by his hair. So, had his head been shaved and the tattoo discovered? If so, what led to the shaving. Or were the authorities already alerted and the tattoo discovered afterwards? Maybe the tattoo was just a harmless adornment mistakenly perceived as… what? Karim didn't know, and not knowing was a problem, a side effect of the thousands of hours put in at the Archive. Others had suffered it too. It was never the intention of the Vision, but not knowing was increasingly seen as a mark of shame.

'Kappa is the 10th letter of the Greek alphabet, used to represent the voiceless velar plosive.'

Karim started and turned toward the speaker. It was the same floppy fringed server who had brought their breakfast and regaled them with everything she knew about cats. Except this time her voice was hushed and her words pregnant with meaning.

'Kappa is Finnish for pelmet. Also, Kappa is a Japanese water spirit. Its form is that of a cross between human, duck, and turtle. Kappas live in ponds and rivers. They drag people in and drown them. If a Kappa gets hold of you it will pull your intestines out through your arsehole. I've no idea why it would do such a thing. But then, why was T Vasily 03 designated for Transit? Does it have something to do with the Quantum Experiments? I say it again: can a cat really be alive and dead at the same time? How many times must they test a theory before it becomes a fact? I recommend the passion juice. The fruit was picked from the farm on Deck H and freshly squeezed this morning.'

Then she was gone.

For a full minute, Karim remained motionless, one hand lifting a cup to the fresh drinks machine. It was as if someone had been listening in on his thoughts, the intrusive ones that shouldered their way through the cognitive flotsam that had cluttered his mind since he was brought to the Station, assessed, and placed on the Archive programme. Was it all too good to be true?

It had been his heart's desire to escape to a safe place. He'd known the risks that came with trusting the traffickers. He'd taken the glorious promise of a golden future with a large pinch of salt but an even larger pitcher of hope. He'd seen how incomers had been treated in his own country. He'd witnessed how those who'd been incomers a generation before went on to look down on the new wave of the desperate and displaced. Instead of experiencing compassion born out of empathy, the new waves were treated with contempt. Those who had felt the same vulnerability, the same fragility, those who had once been in the very same situation, now clutched at a pitiful sense of superiority and were the first to complain about incomers. They had assimilated, aligned themselves with those who had welcomed them in, but then eaten from the tree of the lemon, spitting at those who came to line the streets to merely exist in detention centres and filthy hostels, waiting for their hope of a new life to be realised.

There is a choice in life, Karim knew, between offering a helping hand or a down treading foot. There was also a third way. Karim had chosen that third way: to stay neutral. Throughout the journey from his home, across the vast stretches of barren landscapes and dried up waterways, he had kept himself to himself, promising that when he reached the safety he was seeking he would go back to being his old self: Karim with the smiling eyes. Karim of the kind word. Karim the peacekeeper.

'What's the hold up?'

Bonnar's growl jerked Karim back to the present.

'I was trying to decide. Passionfruit or elder.'

'Neither.'

Bonnar reached for a coffee mug, knocking Karim to one side.

'You know your problem, Transient? You think too much.'

Karim couldn't argue with that. He ignored Bonnar's relish at the new-found way to acknowledge him and lifted a glass to the elderflower dispenser. He watched as the light caught the pale, golden liquid as it flowed into his glass. It seemed to him it was almost the colour of the honey his grandmother had drizzled across her fresh baked bread back in the old country. Honey from the hives on their own land. A land lost years before. He knew this place would never be home, but it was a life. A life his family did not have. Karim choked back the sting of survivor's guilt and set his jaw. The past is past. This is now. The old Karim is not dead, but the new Karim is alive and well. Maybe ignorance is bliss, he thought. Maybe his was not to reason why. Maybe he should just be grateful he had survived. If those Transients had to be designated for annihilation, maybe there was a good reason for it. And if the system had made a mistake, well, it was beyond his pay grade to fret.

Karim cradled his drink in both hands, rolling the cool glass back and forth over his fingers. As he sipped, then heartily gulped, he thought of the old country, and his heart felt almost at peace. Then the antiquated comms sputtered back into life, announcing with an almost imperceptible note of satisfaction:

'T Vasily 03 has logged in.'

WHY I WRITE AND WHY I DRINK

Rob Magnuson Smith

SOME TIME ago, I wrote puff pieces for the drinks trade in exchange for cash, holidays or free booze. On a press junket to a top distillery in Islay, I realized why it is that I write, and why it is that I drink. The revelation hit me in the oldest whisky cellar on the planet, where I was covering the release of a rare 1957 single malt that would eventually sell for $150,000 a bottle.

Mine was a private tasting – just the distillery manager and me – in a cellar below sea level where whisky breathes through the casks, picks up flavours of Spanish oak and matures at its own pace. All writers for the release were promised drams of whatever we wanted, but only one solitary sip of the coveted '57.

The manager led me between the barrels, aging away on their tall wooden racks. The prized hogshead stood in the distance under a spotlight. On my writing and drinking table, a jug of water and dram glass waited beside a pad of paper and ballpoint pen. The twitches crept across my lips. For twenty-four hours, I'd abstained for fresh taste buds and a clear mind.

In the fourteenth century, whisky emerged in Scotland – the Irish dispute the claim – when the hereditary MacBeath clan of medical professionals produced a distillation using mythical herbal lore. Whisky is a relatively simple concoction. The only three recognized ingredients are water, barley, and yeast. These days, of course, everything from mashing to storage is analysed at a molecular level. The premier single malts are created, debated, and refined, again and again, like an overly workshopped poem, long before bottling.

I can still hear the distillery manager's steady tap, tap, tap as he banged open the bung on the hogshead with his wooden hammer. He dipped his glass *valenche* into the barrel and held out my sip. The vintage carried an ominous colour of rich, dark caramel. He poured the whisky into the sipping dram, waited for the last drop to plop into the glass, and stepped back.

I took my post under the spotlight. I held up the glass. The manager looked away, as if to allow the two of us space – my drink, and my writing self – as I brought the aroma to my nose.

I hesitated and put the glass down. It was nerves. More words have been written about whisky than any other spirit. The crowded descriptive space features ludicrous claims, strained similes and comical hyperboles. I heard a voice – *my own voice* – telling me not to bother.

As a writer and a drinker, I had entered the maelstrom. The waves crashed against the distillery walls, and a revelation came: I write, and I drink, because I am uncomfortable in the presence of my own self.

George Orwell claimed, 'One cannot write anything readable, unless one constantly struggles to efface one's personality.' I have acquired a lifelong companion in this struggle. The effacement from a well-constructed sentence equals that of a drink. The writing and the drinking work on independent tracks toward the same goal – so that I can become other.

I am still learning to understand how words and drinks have such power to displace me. Every day, I want to gorge myself with them, whether printed or pixelated, decanted or poured. So I have learned to respect certain rules.

Quality matters. The best writing invites interpretation, challenging our ability to comprehend the forces behind them. Unique or complex drinks have the same capacity, inviting us into an experience we only partially understand, and reconstituting us as we try.

Amount matters. I have underwritten scenes or made only a cursory exploration of a subject or character, and left the reader wanting. Likewise, I sometimes dabble with a small drink, overcautiously taking too little to do any good.

On the other hand, too much writing or drinking reveals a lack of control. After writing binges, I discover on my desk a record of manic enthusiasm. Someone inside me created those unpublishable passages, but who? His cousin has a three-word vocabulary. He says, 'Have a drink.' The morning after, I take out the empties in pain. Perhaps every binge writer and drinker hides a weaker self, a vulnerable sap unable to resist the false friends he fears but cannot avoid.

It's true that my drinking sometimes interferes with my writing. More often, my writing interferes with my drinking. If I am making a good run at an article, shaping a story or finishing a chapter in a novel, my urge for a drink disappears. I enter a kind of trance similar to being drunk. Scenes appear unbeckoned. Pages of dialogue flow rapid and true. I look up at the clock to find hours have passed, without the intrusion of my own needling thoughts. It's like a pint in a pub, or cocktails with friends. I am together with characters cultivated with love. I listen to their stories. I laugh at their idiosyncrasies. I am drowned in the wonderful cacophony of other voices.

During the shifting lockdowns of pandemic Britain, I wrote and I drank even more than I should have. This increase was due to the stifling closeness of myself – a singularly frightening experience. To try and get away, I chased words with drinks, and followed drinks with more words.

I should have read the warning signs. Whenever I produce material I know to be subpar, I write and drink too heavily. It happened once before, in the immediate aftermath of divorce. To avoid financial collapse, I worked hard: editing manuscripts for literary consultancies, hustling commissions for any magazine still in business, ghost-writing novels for which mediocrity was rewarded. Writing for others eclipsed the novel I'd neglected, the short stories orphaned.

Excessive writing produced excessive drinking. Or was it the other way around? During my divorce, it went like this: I woke at dawn and worked all morning. Lunch might have happened. By sunset, I'd had four or five pints at my local, followed by a bottle of wine with dinner – or, no dinner to keep on drinking. Typically, this meant a stack of double gin martinis followed by a life-and-death sprint back to my local before last orders.

During the pandemic I returned to these habits, only at home. Further misdeeds arose like foul fumes in the attempt to combine writing and drinking alchemically, yielding what I can only describe as toxic poetry: wobbly life-writing, laden with authorial indiscretions, and a drunken avoidance of any responsibility for my protagonist.

I relay these facts with no particular alarm. The quantity of my writing and drinking does not seem inordinate, only true to my needs. I certainly don't boast, like some writers and drinkers, of the number of books penned or shots drained. I do want to avoid becoming a drinker like my father, who in his last years drank morning to night, cleanly divided by a midday purge. One eye of mine keeps watch on this inheritance, even as the eye itself grows foggy.

I am also aware of certain danger areas. I tend to drink more at social occasions, especially literary ones. The combination of writers and alcohol can create the most hideous circumstances, further duplicating the worst elements of my personality and my chronic need to escape the sound of my own thoughts. Going to book launches, or conferences where writers stand around the bar, talking about recently published books, or recently signed book deals, or even books-in-progress, makes me drink in extremely high amounts.

When the evening is young, my increased thirst carries a thrill of doing two things I love at the same time: discussing literature, and drinking. This pairing carries a short and poisonous shelf life. I should know to leave early. Instead, I stay at the bar, escaping myself in plain sight.

I have also learned not to entertain old romantic notions of the drunk writer. Those who say the best writers drink are sloppy thinkers. Sure, literary luminaries like Dorothy Parker, William Faulkner and Tennessee Williams were famous alcoholics. More were not – Shakespeare, Milton, Haldor Laxness, Flannery O'Connor. It's not the drinking behind good work, it's adhering to Kierkegaard's faith in the strength of the absurd, reading widely, and logging time at the desk. No matter how well you write, alcohol will eventually sap your vitality. Finally, it removes the self. A few years before his death, F Scott Fitzgerald confessed, 'there was not an *I* anymore – not a basis on which I could organize my self-respect – save my limitless capacity for toil.'

Many tragic heroes provide guidance. Malcolm Lowry, the most infamous writer-drinker, happens to be my favourite British novelist. You'd have to be a fool to suggest *Under the Volcano* could have been written without excess alcohol. Most passages of this gimlet-eyed, hallucinatory novel were influenced by extended binges of mescal, tequila, gin, cheap beer – anything Lowry could get his hands on. Perhaps no other writer drank in such miraculous fashion. He drank for weeks on end. He drank and awoke in different countries. In the end, he died from his addiction as many alcoholic writers do, chasing the decay of booze-induced visions.

Underneath Lowry's impulse to write, I'd wager, boiled good old-fashioned self-loathing. This was the opinion of his mentor, the Jungian poet laureate of the American South, Conrad Aiken, who harnessed his own alcoholic alter-ego for the page. Aiken's writing and drinking came from the same self-annihilating source. He never let himself forget, for artistic reasons, the bright Savannah morning when he was awoken at the age of nine by gunshots. Walking down the corridor to his parents' bedroom, he found them dead. They'd had yet another drunken squabble and wrote out the plot of their murder-suicide.

Writing about the rarest bottled whisky on Islay should have been fun. When asked to join the press junket, I imagined all the pleasures I'd have. I pictured my name in print, testifying in poetic language to the calibre of the vintage. But there is a difference between a simple pleasure, and one that only relieves anxiety. The former presupposes a unified self. The latter points to its fragmentation.

What are new flavours? What is the self? At the moment we taste something unique, we are forever changed. Perhaps it is the case that all of us run away, at every chance, from our so-called original selves – through work, reading and writing literature, watching films, tasting wine, or reproducing yet another self and hoping for the best. I conned myself into believing that a press junket to Islay would extend my creative work. These blandishments were simply the components of an elaborate rationalisation, my personal defense mechanism of choice.

That morning at the hogshead, my rationalisations were broken wide open. The fog cleared, and I finally understood. My writing and my drinking were cloaking devices. They needed to be exposed and reconciled, or I was in danger of disappearing entirely.

'The chemists think they're onto what happens in these casks,' the distillery manager told me, as I stood there frozen at my table. He had a soft, feathery voice. He reminded me of those medics who relieve anxiety by talking about the mundane. He told me his first job had been digging drains outside the distillery, forty-six years ago. 'I hope they never find out what goes on with this whisky,' he said. 'If they ever do, they'll fix it to suit themselves.'

I asked him a few questions about the '57 vintage. I expected routine replies to do with peat smoke and barrel time in Spanish sherry oak. He was more interested in discussing fiction.

'You're a novelist, aren't you?' he asked. 'What are you working on at the moment?'

I stared at the dram in my hand. I told him about my novel *Scorper*, about a disturbed American chasing after his ancestral roots in Sussex. It would come out the following year. 'My protagonist has psychological issues,' I said. 'Insecurities about life.'

'I thought that was your first novel.'

'That was about a gravedigger.'

'Oh. You've made progress, then.'

In 1957, eight years after winning the Nobel and short on funds, William Faulkner began a two-week lectureship at the University of Virginia. The first night, he stepped to the bar to pay his five-dollar tab. The next night, he hailed the bartender to pay. Not necessary, he was told, five dollars was to be his flat bar bill – for all fourteen days of his residence.

Faulkner reportedly went white as a sheet. He had twelve days of free booze before him, and he knew what that entailed. 'Aw, no,' he reportedly said, slowly shaking his head. 'That just ain't *right*.'

Writers are experts at deception. They deceive

others, and they deceive themselves. If you dangle something desirable under their noses, such as money and publication, they improve at their own game. When offered something too good, this self-deception comes crashing down. They sniff danger – a danger that lies within.

Writing and drinking to efface the self means that highs are soon followed by lows. In 2004, after I inexplicably won an award for my manuscript *The Gravedigger*, I was flown to New Orleans, handed a check for $10,000, and draped with a gold medal embossed with Faulkner's profile. Top editors and agents from New York appeared at my side. They were the very ones I'd already sent my manuscript to, months before, without reply.

Naturally, I became over-excited. Nervous, arrogant, over-confident and insecure, both grateful and suspicious of their company, I simply drank, and drank, and drank, for five straight days. I didn't eat. I just drank. A few kind souls tried to intervene. The organisers assigned me a 'minder', a Vietnam War vet and Pulitzer Prize winner, but even he gave up. When I looked around, at the end of my unveiling, the agents and editors had gone.

I had done it – manifested my low self-worth, and made my fears come true. Nobody would ever want to publish my work now. The next logical step was projection. I angrily decided they weren't worth my attention. And I set out to prove it.

It was the lowest point in my literary life. I have an unfortunately clear memory of tracking them down to tell them off. Still wearing the medal around my neck, I stormed out into the night. They hadn't gone far. There they all were, the top literary agents and heads of publishing houses sharing a bank of tables in an exclusive French Quarter bar. Seeing me stumble toward them, they suddenly went quiet.

Finger wagging, I listed the worst novels they had recently published, one after the other. They had betrayed their calling, I told them. They didn't really care about the written word.

'It's actual dog shit you've been publishing,' I said. 'Literary *dog shit*.'

My bar bill at the end of my stay in New Orleans came to $1145. Checking out of the hotel, I held the document in my trembling hands. It was a paper river of gin martinis. Each had its own time stamp. Between noon and midnight, each day, I'd drunk enough to kill myself. It would be six years before I found an agent across the Atlantic willing to look at my so-called winning manuscript, and eight years before the novel finally appeared.

The distillery manager smiled as I still struggled to begin. 'After that '57,' he said, 'you know you can taste anything you like.' He waved up at the wooden racks, rising like the archways of a cathedral, where hundreds of silent hogsheads nestled in their chambers. 'You know, to get some context. Over a hundred years of single malts, just for you.'

'Aw, no,' I muttered. 'That just ain't right.'

It must have showed that I was nervous. The only writers worth anything were poets – my dad's refrain. He had tried his hand, of course. *He* knew. Of all those published, he'd insisted, only a handful ever meant anything. The rest, he liked to say, were nothing more than dog shit.

I was writing the last chapter of *The Gravedigger* when he collapsed under a hedge in Worcestershire. He'd been barred from his local and walked eight miles to get served, then died of a heart attack walking home. The day before, he had burned everything he owned in one of his many acts of suicidal rage. Maybe he too had voices he wanted gone. During his last years he stopped reading his favourite poems. He no longer drank English ale, but the most rancid scrumpy. He carried a heady stench of this sour concoction which corroded nasal passages. When they found his body, he had no ID, making his own self-effacement come true. He remained unidentified in the morgue for weeks.

I finished the novel. I buried the man. I had worked as an apprentice gravedigger for research and knew what to do. Not long after, I won the Faulkner prize.

There wasn't even a short-lived triumph. Apparently, the sudden death of a parent can create an 'incomplete mourning,' a fractured self that widens if not reconciled. William Styron wrote, 'Such reconciliation may be entwined with the quest for immortality…no less than that of a writer of fiction, to vanquish death through work honoured by posterity.'

Posterity from work – what a strange, delusional, if comforting concept, probably invented by fiction writers. Recently, my third novel *Seaweed Rising* finally appeared. It wasn't an easy process. The same agent who took on *The Gravedigger* and sold *Scorper* told me the novel was too strange. The writer she'd signed on was unrecognisable. I can't imagine anyone will publish it, she warned me.

It's true that 'I' had become someone else. So I found another agent, someone who found the novel strange in a good way. I wrote this novel, I explained, because I know that seaweeds are coming for me. They're coming for all of us. I know this because I sleep with them. They surround the boat I live on. They creep toward my head each night, waiting for the end. He understood. Writing and drinking can unveil all sorts of terrors.

'Go on, then,' the distillery manager urged, down in the cellar. 'Give it a go.' He politely averted his gaze again.

I lifted the glass to my nose. This time, the aroma evoked desire. I closed my eyes and saw a field of wildflowers. I heard bees, and smelled honey. In the vault stood a man with an awakening palate, a man who realised he'd never really had whisky, not like this. It was the stuff of epiphanies.

One smell of the '57 created a wish for life, for love, for immortality. Sipping it – well, that uncovered the substratum. There were three discrete stages: the embrace of a delicate mouthfeel, followed by pine smoke along the palate, then a long, lingering finish of sea salt. And pepper. And caramel. And heather. I chased that complex finish up and down the vault, never to find it again. My taste buds were both awakened and tormented, long after my flight home.

Back in my flat, I had a difficult time writing the article. Even though I'd made my tasting notes, I was stuck. I usually wrap up my shorter pieces in one or two sittings, but as the hours passed, I still couldn't do the vintage justice. My father stood in my mind's eye, waiting for mistakes. I was both exposed and returned to myself, and the unwanted voices had grown louder.

The distillery manager had given me a bottle of

their signature 12-year Scotch to take home. I went into the kitchen and poured myself a double. I still hadn't had breakfast. So I write and I drink because I want to be erased, I told myself. Now it seemed impossible – the mirror just wouldn't go away. Holding the whisky above my dirty dishes, I consulted a darker future. I couldn't hear the waves of Islay. I couldn't see fields or bees. I only smelled epitaphs on gravestones, and wet soil. After a moment, I put the glass down. I covered it with a tea towel, like silencing a parrot.

I returned to my desk. I wrote and wrote. Gradually, my self dissolved in the only way that gives me peace. With each sentence, a new person emerged that thwarted the last, the one that forever tells me I'm useless. The voices of creation and annihilation reached a temporary agreement.

This is what writing does. It permits us to find our way, the morning after. It leads us away from our old selves in a continuous journey of insights, experiments and amendments. Perhaps the effort alone proves we are never completely effaced.

It is also what drinking can do. After I filed my piece, the beautiful cocktail sunset came at last. I returned to my kitchen. I released my whisky glass from its cage. I drank, poured another, and drank again. This time, I didn't have to write about it. I just introduced the multiple voices in my mind, like so many arrivals to a party, and listened at a distance.

GIFT FROM THE SEA

Emma Timpany

THIS BEACH hasn't changed – it's the same slim strip of coarse-grained, pinkish sand in a black rock cove as curved as an eye. There's something about the sound of the waves, the crumbling clay cliffs. Voices carry on the wind, a blur of words from the coast path above. Ponies graze the cliff meadows amongst the bracken and bee orchids.

I wouldn't say that I come here to think – quite the opposite. Here, things are simpler. Here, perhaps, I could slip off this false carapace and canter off, crabwise, to the waves. Here, like the sand, I take only what I am given. On the tideline, the familiar tell, a colour tender as baby flesh. On my knees I sift and scoop, picking out tiny cowries, their curving shells the pale pink of a summer dawn as the hot hand of the sun presses down on my back.

Further up the beach, I've left the pile of bags I carried here. Red rifts stripe my palms from carrying their awkward weight over rocks and sand. It's all in the bags, what I owe you, what I stole from you and have hidden for so long. I'm no better than my aunt, twisting the rings from her dead mother's fingers, hiding them away from her siblings, those bands of dark old gold set with a galaxy of rubies, sapphires and diamonds. Rings which I coveted. Rings that also were taken from me.

I turn from my sifting and lean back on the bags. It's uncomfortable resting on a nest of jutting points which dig into my skin. Out in the bay, a seal breaks the surface and sea water pours silkily from its face. Grebes and divers dip beneath the waves and reemerge some distance away. The sea's surface is oily in the heat, viscous as it pours over the black tips of reef-like rocks. The haunted summer wind brushes the exposed rocks of the littoral. Closed sea anemones cluster on the rocks, wet and red.

If anyone can do it, you will find me here. This beach is the place I've chosen for a reckoning with you. Even now you may have begun picking your way over the rocks from Carne. You probably think I'll give them back to you, but these you won't have. No one will – that's why I'm here.

Until a week ago, I hadn't been inside my father's house for fifteen years. I knew that he was dying. I clean the doctor's surgery; it's one of many places I work. I'm a shadow, slipping in and out of view before the day arrives. I read his file, saw the many illnesses held in his body like cards pulled from a stacked deck, a royal flush, and so I started watching his house again, early and late.

I live in a wind-soaked former holiday chalet on the cliffs. When the trees are bare, I can glimpse the glittering turrets of my father's creekside home in the valley, watch his lights going on and off in the daytime and by night. As the end approached, they flickered rapidly, a lighthouse flash of danger and distress. I felt as brimful as a cream-coloured sky before a snowfall. Finally, I smelt the possibility of victory – as if, for all these years, all that had been needed was the right combination of atmospheric pressure, a cold easterly meeting a warm storm wind from the west.

In this world, there's so much muck and dirt to be dislodged. Every day I clean and sweep and the next day there it is again, an endless rain of dirt and dead skin cells. I drive to the accompanying rattle of buckets and mops in the back of my chewed-up Nissan Micra, my Henry hoover riding shotgun in the passenger seat, and a basket of disinfectant, cloths and window cleaner in the footwell.

That morning, I parked a little way up the road and took the old path through the woods. Along the silted creekside, I walked beneath a richness of August blackberries and dark-leaved elder. During my visits, I'd worn a groove on the black earth, a furrow made by an animal trying to return to its fold. Clouds mustered above me, all dreamy shades of bruise and smoke. I sniffed the wind, warm and rain-laden, and felt it lift my hair. The lights in my father's house. Off and on. Off and then, as the clouds darkened, a river of light flowed from the top floor to the front door. An ambulance rumbled up over potholes and parked under the portico, yellow and waddly as a bath duck, splashed by the mud of the lane. Puddy opened the door to let in two muscly, green uniformed paramedics, my grandmother's rings aglitter on her fingers.

A gurney. A bluebell-coloured vinyl medical glove dropped on the dim gravel of the drive. A blanket, cherry red, over the prone figure of my father. An oxygen tank. His blanched face, beneath the straps of the mask. Off they went. Puddy stood for a moment, stunned but jerking slightly, as if tazered. She went back inside. Keys, bag, coat. Minutes later, her nifty silver Mercedes A-type departed, and it began to rain.

I was up for breaking a window. I was up for anything, but the door opened to my touch and I stepped onto the familiar floor of brick-red and lava-grey encaustic tiles. Puddy's dogs, a mother and daughter pair of black Labradors, roused themselves. We knew each other well, having had many encounters in the woods. I pulled their favourite treats from my smock pockets and let them lick my hands.

On the wall above the limestone mantel carved with a running wave was the painting I had come for, an impasto field of off-whites and blurry creams, its sister piece sold to the Tate for over a million last year. Despite its heavy look, it was light in my arms after I untethered it from the wall.

While searching for large bin bags in which to stash my loot, I found the little room under the stairs next to the same old wretched loo Puddy had done little to improve. In what used to be the butler's pantry was a recently vacated single bed and a bedside table covered by a thicket of pill bottles. This was where the old beast had ended up, then, in a damp, dark hole, with bars on its ivy-covered window.

Oh, but on the dismal walls such treasure hung. Small, square paintings not much wider than a large man's hand span which glittered like icons in smoky Byzantine churches. Each contained an image you could tumble into headfirst. My favourite showed bands of colour – beaten silver, taupe, aubergine –

laid inside each other, becoming smaller and smaller until they disappeared to a vanishing point, a shimmering hallway down which a soul could pass before melting into the lamp black silence at its centre.

I saw at once what they were: his songs of praise, his secret chords. His mitigation lest he face divine judgement for his faithlessness. The terror of death, of all he wrongs he'd committed, was written in these blazing squares. I took all of them. Every single one. If he ever returns to this place, he'll find his *sanctum sanctorum* empty. A drawing board, a desk, a plans chest, a creaking floorboard beneath damp Axminster. By his sketchpad, a stick of charcoal. I picked it up and wrote *God hates you* on the wall.

Doctor Seth knows of our connection, and she's always been kind to me. When Mum died, she got me counselling and helped me sort myself out. Sick note after sick note for a while, but the doctor never got fed up with me. She understood when I told her I was going away. 'But you'll come back,' she said. 'This is your home, too.'

When she gave me the job, she said nothing more than the usual about confidentiality. She's the only one who ever speaks to me about my mother, who even seems to remember her. Doctor Seth smells nice, like vanilla and sea salt mixed up and warmed. Towards the end, my mother had a kind of chemical tang about her, a smell which disappeared briefly each time they pulled her from the sea.

Lots of people go crazy, but they lose their minds in different ways. My mother peeled potatoes until peelings were all that remained. She left doors and windows open in all weathers, asked if I could hear the buzzing from the underground cables carrying messages beneath the waves to America. The radar discs were tracking her, scanning secrets from the grey, damp forests of her brain. She went shopping and came back days later. Wet. Every time, wet through, and it hadn't always been raining. And the reason for it never occurred to me, quite honestly. I was thirteen. And thirteen-year-olds notice everything, but they can't always fit the pieces together. No-one said, Your mother is ill. In and out of the water. In and out of hospital. Always released to try again, relentless as the waves.

When my mother died, my father and Puddy wouldn't take me in, because Puddy had given birth to you by then. I went from place to place. When the system released me, I moved to this chalet. Last winter, something shook loose, and I opened the old boxes containing my mother's papers. Child support payments never made. Rent arrears, last notice electricity and gas bills. All those years of struggle, and my father never gave us a penny. He employed every deceit imaginable, an arrow shower of lies from my family of thieves.

What a shame there's no money in art. The house with the turrets, glittering in the valley, was in Puddy's name. The rest – millions, probably – is untouchable, hidden away in some trust. Gleaming gold and gems on the soft skin of Puddy's fingers. Waiting, watching. Puddy and my father. Ink-black darkness pouring through me each time I saw them hand in hand in the village or on the moss path to St Wyllow.

When my mother was a girl, the locals dumped their rubbish on this beach. The tide came up and carried it away. Traces remain at low water and after winter storms – odd, rusted coils of bedsprings, bucket-shaped lumps of concrete. Amongst it, tiny basslings hide in purple shadows.

I started collecting driftwood in spring. There's quite a pile, now. Logs, timber, broken pallets. Brushwood from the cliffs. The sea's refuse. All summer I've been planning today's great blaze. You'll see the light, the smoke, despite the glare of the setting sun.

The big painting of the white field from above my father's fireplace is the first to go. On this beach where, for the last time, my mother walked into the water, I place it on the pyre. The others follow, khaki and zinc, slashes of lamp black, crimson screams.

It's the final piece that troubles me, the first

painting I saw in the little room under the stairs of a beautiful hallway leading to an inner blackness. At the centre of the marble-clad temples in Greece and Rome there was always a room for the god to inhabit, a circular space full of darkness, entirely enclosed. No windows. No doors. The most sacred place in the building was lightless and empty, a sealed centre containing nothing.

Cooler air moves over the sea, raising a light fog which dims the sun's intensity. For a second, the air turns the peculiar, grainy black of eclipse light, and in this strange moment the painting opens its arms to me. It tells me my father was sorry. From its surface rises some bitter scent I recognise, preservative as salt, metallic as the lead-lined coffins of the contaminated dead.

No mercy. I hurl it on top of the pyre and grab the container of fuel the farmer has chained to the rock next to his boat and lobster pots. The currents in this bay are known for dragging the litter away, casting them off into the depths, never to be seen again. My mother remembered eventually. A fitting place for local trash.

Over the sea, a violet sky. A half-moon ghosts the upper cliff. Amongst the dark blocks of container ships, a blaze of lemon horizon. Time for me to light my beacon. Last sun on the white sands of Carne, the hotel guests in their robes dissolving into silver mirages. A beach of small, safe waves. You white-blond and brown-shouldered; the gulls and the campion nodding. The verdancy of gorse, remedy for the broken-hearted.

It's falling back to earth now, water vapour that's spent all day rising up into the blue. The matches are damp but the third one lights and tosses its bright head of flame high. I edge back. Such intensity already, huge, hurting sparks and cracks of splintering wood driving me seaward until my feet touch water. A huge bang as debris blasts everywhere and I turn and dive.

Slack tide. I made sure of that. I'm not ready for the currents to take me yet. I deserve one triumph in this pitiless life. I stole what I could never benefit by, had only power to destroy. Whose fault is that? It's only paint and canvas after all. His legacy. Your inheritance. And mine.

Perhaps you'll come in time to douse the flames; you have that kind of golden air about you. Perhaps you'll save the day somehow, the young knight errant that you are. Perhaps the flames themselves will refuse the dirty work I've given them to do, and, of their own accord, subside and die. I don't care. I've made my point. Time to disappear.

You were the only one who saw me. When you walked with them in the woods, tiny and unsure, my father on one side of you, Puddy on the other. One, two, three, weeeee! Up you swung. You were the one who paused, looked back, sensed the watcher in the shadows, and said nothing at all while they cooed like pigeons above your bright head. You peered out of your bedroom window on lilac-skied summer evenings, pulling back the curtain when you should have been asleep, opening the window wide. Your eyes searched the field at the edge of the woods, the drystone wall, the shivering branches of beech. You sensed me in the supermarket, the shapeless worker moving quickly out of your path, the shadowy figure wiping clean a pane of smudged glass.

Friendship was your offer. The kindness I had never been shown. Restitution for the unfairness I'd suffered at the hands of your mother, our father. You wanted to see me, to get to know me, to try to make amends. This is my answer to you. I am not worth it. I stole from you to steal from them. I burned what I could never own, works of art which could only ever belong to you no matter what you said.

Neck deep. The current shifts again, a landward push. The tide's rough hand, surging up the sand, into the coming dark. And I see you, torch in hand. You've always known what we both needed. You've waited for me as I've waited for you. I mistake the sharp prod to my chest for the thumping of my misshapen heart until I see my spirit painting – the glittering hallway and infinite centre – floating on the water. With a pulse the tide presses it to me as your hand wraps itself in mine.

A BORDER INCIDENT

Tim Hannigan

YOU KNOW the trees I mean. On that first deep stretch of the A30 heading west, after the tawny shoulders of Dartmoor have fallen behind; the stretch that always seems longer than you remembered, though it's hard to keep the needle from nudging towards ninety.

And then, just as you begin to despair of ever getting through the billowing infinity of Devon, there they are: a spinney of slender beeches, slewed off the crown of a small rise where the dual carriageway bends to the right. They look like the remnants of an army, a last centuria at bay. And as they whip past on the passenger side you know that inside of three minutes you'll be barrelling across the Tamar and up the rise onto home ground.

There are other way-markers, of course, multiplying and diverging as we swing left and right off the grand trunk, narrowing to the tendrils of the purely personal. I have some eighty miles of them still to go: the point where the western half of Cornwall opens ahead on the edge of the clay country; the rough gauge of current tide times with a rightward glance at Hayle; the wind-whipped blackthorn on the hedge at Bull's View; and the final rise from the Mên-an-Tol lay-by to the point where the ocean opens ahead.

But the trees are the first. A rousing signal: almost home. You might make some flashing obeisance to them as you pass, or at very least offer a nod of acknowledgment. And three miles outside of Cornwall, they are common to every traveller who crosses the Tamar.

On a heavy August afternoon, heading homewards, I finally did something I've long been minded to do: at the first distant glimpse of the trees I swung south off the A30, pulled in at the side of a quiet road, unfolded the map, and tried to work out how to reach them.

The trees, I believe, are known as Cookworthy Knapp, but the Ordnance Survey gave them no name. This was the cause of a small outrage. I felt that they should be marked with some portentous symbol – a pair of crossed flags, perhaps, of the sort that guidebooks use to show international border crossings. But they were scarcely even present on the sheet: the smallest dab of green, sitting on the 120-metre contour line and containing a single *non-coniferous tree* and seven miniscule scratchings suggesting some kind of pit. And to get to them, I would have to go the long way around.

This was Devon at its deepest. The knapped blue lanes seemed to have fallen, ten, twenty, thirty feet down into the clammy base layers of a blanketing jungle. The contours were as convoluted as those of a human brain, but there wasn't a single hard edge to knock against. Once or twice I saw the trees, suddenly leaping into distant view across the groundswell of the country, as distinctive from this side as from the other. They'd chosen their defensive spot well: I had little chance of creeping up on them.

A lone cow at the bottom of a long field. A faint smell of treacle rising from the verges. White signposts to *stows* and *hams* and *cotts* – the nomenclature of another Anglo-Saxon land, without the familiar Cornish *tre* and *bos* and *pen* that would begin just a few miles further west. A glimpse of two policemen, thumbs hitched to their shoulders, bending at the door of a shop in an empty village; then a turn into a narrower lane.

The hedges were still higher here, and the foliage

pressed tight on either side of the car, brushing at the doors and windows. It was like edging through a silent mob. The trees swam into view again, tall and close, with the light coming through the fence of their trunks. The sky behind them was dishwater-grey. An old blue tractor, expired at the roadside with the weeds growing through the chassis; squalid barns with slurry and straw calcified in deep layers; and then I was on a lane running parallel to the A30, and the trees were standing ahead. They could certainly see me coming.

I drove up onto a grassy bank, and stepped out. There was a gate into the bottom of the long, triangular field which the trees dominated, but I walked towards them up the lane instead. The A30 was whining noisily to the right, but this strip of tarmac carried no traffic. In the hedges: hazels showing a faint rosiness on their crenelated leaves; the port-wine colour of the hawthorn branches behind the green; and blackberries as ripe and melting as foie gras. In the distance behind, Dartmoor faded into sloe-coloured murk.

There was something wrong with the optics of the afternoon. The light was dull, and neither I nor the hedges cast a shadow. But somehow the trees were preternaturally dark, near-black amid the flat grey-green two-tone of the afternoon. I should have taken it as a warning.

At the top of the rise, a muddy gateway, a padlock and a faded 'no entry' sign. Clearly, I wasn't the first person to have had this idea. But the trees were all of fifty feet away beyond the barrier, their great cumulus of foliage shifting darkly in the electric air. There was no one around, and these trees were *our* trees. They might lie in Devon, but it was *we* who nodded at them every time in gratitude for their signal: almost home. Surely, they had the status of an embassy, a little pocket of Cornish territory islanded in an alien land.

I awarded myself diplomatic immunity, vaulted the gate, and was across the strip of pasture in half a minute.

It was like being in a great colonnaded hall. There were maybe 150 trees. Their trunks were slender and supremely tall, none quite true, each wavering slightly like a rocket contrail on its skyward trajectory. High above, the light came as through a vast stained-glass dome, with a susurration and the muffled clatter of wood pigeons on the move.

From the inside, the genius of the spinney's form was plain to see. The trees had been planted – sometime in the nineteenth century, judging by the height of them – with perfect spacing, ten or twelve feet apart, but without any grid arrangement. It gave the thing the perfection that marked it out so clearly from the road – a single compact unit that nonetheless allowed the sky to show through from the furthest side.

The pit marked on the map lay at the eastern edge, open towards the A30 at its lower end. Approaching it from uphill, I thought for a thrilling moment that it was some kind of portal, that it led to a tunnel. But it terminated in a blind slope.

Something about the place made me uneasy. I'd expected a sense of sanctuary, protection. Seen from the road, these were the friendliest of trees, offering encouragement for the home stretch to all passers: *almost there!* But this inner space felt deeply private, exclusive, and I had no share of it. It was the feeling you get when you come unexpectedly upon a site of uncomprehended ritual: burnt-out incense sticks; broken bowls; ragged votive fragments – the kind of place you walk away from with a sickly sense that you may, in your unintended trespass, have picked up an occult contagion.

I stilled such lurid thoughts and sat down at the base of one of the trees to make some notes, but the lingering unease made it hard to concentrate. The main road was in view below, carrying a thick floodtide of caravans. But the hissing canopy overhead managed to block all but the lowest hum, like the sound of beehives on a hot day.

I wrote a date and a first scribbled line, then stopped. There was some other mechanical noise, not from the A30, but from higher up, closer at hand: the harsh clatter of agricultural machinery. A sudden surge of alarm. I was back onto my feet and clutching at the trunk of the tree, trying to shrink behind its slender column. It wasn't so much the 'no entry' sign that had fired the panic, as that faint intimation of the uncanny within the spinney.

The engine noise seemed to be very close, and getting closer. It sounded, in fact, as if it was right at the edge of the trees. I ducked and dipped behind the sheltering trunk, glancing wildly left and right. But the field was empty. Behind me, I could see my car through the lower gateway, five hundred yards downhill, away from the noise of the approaching, but still invisible, engine. Should I hunker down, try to hide? But the spinney was open through and through. It was a wood that offered no cover at all for a fugitive. Was *that* what made it an unsettling place?

The engine was drawing closer still. Why couldn't I see its source? Then finally a flicker of movement on the other side of the uphill hedge: the figure of a man riding some machine. I didn't know if he had seen me, but he might as well have had a bayonet and a grey helmet. These were *not* my woods, and whose woods they were I did *not* know; I was a trespasser here in every sense. With a queasy jolt I understood that theirs had never been a friendly signal to the wayfarers below. I'd smiled doltishly at them countless times in passing without once recognizing their filigreed form for what it so obviously was: *a cage*. I had wandered into a trap…

What happened next is not entirely clear, but I know that suddenly I was fleeing, a mad helter-skelter dash down the slope, pitching forward, away from the trees, in terrified expectation of something from behind – a shout, a shot, a grasping tentacle. Then I was over the lower gate and into the car, fumbling at the ignition with the metallic taste of my heartbeat high in my throat.

In many years of wandering with blithe disregard for rights of way, confident in my ability to signal that I am, in fact, from this side of the border, that *I'm* alright to walk across these fields even if *they're* not, I have never experienced such a moment of unhinged panic. I could make no sense of it.

I drove on up the lane the way I had earlier walked – the quickest route back to the A30, it seemed from the map. My hands were unsteady on the wheel. I passed the higher gateway with the 'no entry' sign, and then a second gateway into the next field. There was no sign of any man or any machine.

It was only hours later, eighty miles to the west, lying in my bed, that it struck me. Chances are that there was someone who knew the spinney driving westward along the A30 at a particular moment on that heavy August afternoon. And as they raised their head to the left, feeling the small surge that comes with the first signal of home, they would have seen something strange, inexplicable, even uncanny: a small figure, pelting away from the trees, propelled by the unmistakable velocity of terror. Surely the unexplained image, torn past at 80 miles an hour, would have left them faintly unnerved. Perhaps they carried that unease on westwards, across the Tamar, across Bodmin Moor, past all the other signals, all the way home. Perhaps at that same moment, lying in their own bed at journey's end, somewhere not so far away, the image was playing out again and again on the backs of their eyelids, fixing itself in their memory as a small, unquiet scar: a madly fleeing figure on a green hillside beneath the border trees. Who was he? What was he running from? *And did he escape?*

It may be, then, that there are now two people who will never look at those trees in quite the same way, ever again.

ABOUT THE CONTRIBUTORS

Rebecca Johnson Bista lives in West Penwith, Cornwall, where she writes poetry and fiction and is completing her first novel. Her work has been published in *One Hand Clapping, Words with Jam, Aspier*, and *The Broadsheet*. Rebecca originally studied English Literature at Oxford and is currently undertaking a PhD in illness narratives at Exeter University.

Anastasia Gammon lives in Cornwall, somewhere between the moors and the sea. Her short fiction has been published by *Daily Science Fiction*, *Popshot Quarterly*, *PaperBound Magazine*, and in *Cornish Short Stories: A Collection of Contemporary Cornish Writing*, as well as many other places online. She is currently working on a YA contemporary fantasy novel set in Cornwall.

Tim Hannigan was born in Penzance and is the author of several narrative history books including *Murder in the Hindu Kush, Raffles and the British Invasion of Java*, and *A Brief History of Indonesia*. He also edited and expanded *A Brief History of Bali* and wrote *A Geek in Indonesia*. His latest book is *The Granite Kingdom*.

Kate Horsley's first novel, *The Monster's Wife*, was shortlisted for the Scottish First Book of the Year Award. Her second novel, *The American Girl*, was published by William Morrow and translated into Korean by Tomato Publishing. All her longer fiction has been optioned for film and television. Kate studied English Literature at Oxford and holds a PhD from Harvard.

Clare Howdle is a writer and editor who lives by the sea and is drawn to its stories. Her fiction has been listed for the Lucy Cavendish Prize, the Masters Review Prize, the Mslexia Prize and the Bath Short Story Award. Her stories have been published in the *Sunday Times, Cornish Short Stories, Litro, Riptide* and more. She is currently working on a novel set in Cornwall's wreck diving community.

Adrian Markle is the author of *Bruise,* a novel, and twenty short stories in significant journals and magazines in Canada, the US and Europe, including *Pithead Chapel* and *Riptide*. Those short stories have earned him Best Small Fictions and Pushcart nominations, as well as a place on university curriculums. He is a Creative Writing Lecturer at the University of Falmouth.

Tim Martindale was born and raised in Cornwall. His writing features in *Watermarks: Writing by Lido Lovers and Wild Swimmers*, *Cornish Short Stories: A Collection of Contemporary Writing*, and also in *The Clearing*. He recently completed his first book, *Pathways to Home*, a work of narrative non-fiction exploring themes around belonging, ecology, family and place.

P. T. McAllister's writing blurs the boundary between novel and short story collection. His writing has been shortlisted in international awards and included in numerous journals and anthologies. His debut book is slated for publication. He studied English at the University of Cambridge, was awarded a Distinction for his MA in Creative Writing and is doing his PhD at Exeter University. He is the Morrab Library Writer in Residence.

Rob Magnuson Smith is the author of *The Gravedigger, Scorper*, and *Seaweed Rising*. His short fiction has appeared most recently in *Granta, The Saturday Evening Post, Ploughshares, the Guardian, Fiction International,* and *Guillemot Press*. His prizes include the David Higham Award, the William Faulkner Prize for the novel, and the Elizabeth Jolley Award.

Mark Plummer is a writer from Penwith, in the Celtic west of Cornwall. His short stories have appeared in literary journals and anthologies around the world. He has also co-written and performed in plays for UK arts and literature festivals.

Katherine Stansfield grew up on Bodmin Moor. Her latest solo novel is *The Mermaid's Call*. Katherine's poetry is published by Seren. Her most recent collection is *We Could Be Anywhere by Now,* selected by Wales Literature Exchange as a 'Bookcase' title. She teaches for Faber Academy and has been a Royal Literary Fund fellow.

Jackie Taylor is a writer of poetry, short fiction, and hybrid things who lives and works in Cornwall. Her short story collection, *Strange Waters*, was published in 2021 by Arachne Press. She holds an MLitt in Creative Writing from the University of Glasgow.

Karen Taylor is a UEA alumni crime writer whose Penzance-based serial killer thriller *Fairest Creatures* was longlisted for the 2020 CWA Debut Dagger. *Dark Arts* is its prequel. Also based in Penzance, the book is a thriller which revolves around the local arts community. Karen has one son and two cats and spends her time between London and Penzance.

Shelley Trower worked as a Professor of English Literature at the University of Roehampton before returning to Cornwall. Books include *Senses of Vibration*, *Rocks of Nation*, and *Sound Writing*. Since leaving academia she has published short stories, including 'Seagulls' in *Litro* Magazine, and is currently funded by Arts Council England to develop her novel writing.

Emma Timpany was born and grew up in the far south of Aotearoa New Zealand. She lives in Cornwall. Her publications include the short story collections *Three Roads* and *The Lost of Syros*, a novella *Travelling in the Dark* and *Cornish Short Stories*. Emma's writing has won awards and her work has been published in journals in England, New Zealand and Australia.

Tom Vowler is an award-winning novelist and short story writer living in the UK. A university lecturer with a PhD in creative writing, his work has featured on BBC radio and been translated into multiple languages. His forthcoming book is a collection of flash fiction and he is currently writing a memoir.

Ella Walsworth-Bell lives and works in Cornwall. She has curated two poetry anthologies *Morvoren* and *Mordardh*, about sea swimming and surfing. Her short stories have been published in *Paperbound, Indigo Dreams, Cornwall: Secret and Hidden* and *Cornwall: Beneath and Beyond*. She won the Cornwall Creatives South West Short Story competition.

Elaine Ruth White writes for page, stage and broadcast and has a clinical background in mental health. As well as her theatre work, she has written comedy for the BBC and was the writer on English Touring Opera's award-winning Cornish production *One Day, Two Dawns*. Her first novel, *Unreliable Witness*, was published in 2021.

Becky Wildman grew up in Birmingham, studied English at university and currently lives in Cornwall with her two young boys. The eldest is profoundly disabled, and is a constant source of inspiration. She recently completed her MA in creative writing and is writing a surrealist novel.

Milton Keynes UK
Ingram Content Group UK Ltd.
UKHW050658101224
3551UKWH00029B/197